This special edition of

MEDICINA MAGICA

By Hans Biedermann

has been privately printed
for the members of
The Classics of Medicine Library

Original Austrian edition published by
Akademische Druck- u. Verlagsanstalt, Graz 1972[1], 1978[2]

BIEDERMANN · MEDICINA MAGICA

MEDICINA MAGICA

Hans Biedermann

Metaphysical Healing Methods in
Late-antique and Medieval Manuscripts
With Thirty Facsimile Plates

TRANSLATED FROM THE GERMAN BY ROSEMARIE WERBA

THE CLASSICS OF MEDICINE LIBRARY • DIVISION OF GRYPHON EDITIONS, INC. • BIRMINGHAM, ALABAMA

Printed and published by

Akademische Druck- u. Verlagsanstalt, Graz 1972[1], 1978[2]

Printed in Austria
ISBN 3-201-01077-4

TABLE OF CONTENTS

Introduction 7

Metaphysical Healing Theories 9

The Postulate of the Four Humours 17

The Tacuinum sanitatis 23

Magical and Empirical Drugs 27

Medicina antiqua 33

The Wiener Dioskurides 35

The Pursuance of Harmony 41

Bibliographical References 43

Facsimile Plates 47

    Tacuinum sanitatis (Plates 1–15) 48

    Medicina antiqua (Plates 16–24) 78

    Wiener Dioskurides (Plates 25–30) 96

The History of Medicine is not just one of the disciplines of the larger field of the History of Science; its subject matter is mankind's struggle with the existential problems of illness and death in the course of the history of the world. It appears that from a viewpoint of general philosophical history, important consequences can be derived from the nature of this conflict such as from the history of botany or geology. When we realize under what conditions mankind of past centuries and millennia faced this battle, undiminished in its significance to this day, and when it becomes apparent what positions it was able to assume, we can learn much about the guiding principles and motivations of varied cultural fundamental structures, and perhaps even about our own basic existential problems.

We cannot offer here a complete treatise, only some glimpses with the help of valuable old codices published in the last few years in the form of facsimiles. Publications of this kind are primarily directed toward scientific institutions, are usually limited editions and are, consequently, quite costly. However, an ever growing circle of people with a special interest in culture and history have the desire to participate in the exploration of this source of old pictures and writings.

Therefore, we shall select and discuss from among a few codices those that are significant for the history of medicine, those that concern themselves with a very interesting and until now very neglected aspect of the history of medicine, namely the "medicina magica," with its irrational theories and healing methods dating back to ancient sympathy doctrines, as well as those concerning the impact of folk medicine on pharmacology. Those aspects of the development of the art of healing, that have in many historical studies simply been referred to as, "Erdenrest, zu tragen peinlich," (primitive, embarrassing remains) and put *ad acta*, will serve here to enrich the philosophical history with more than just a number of folkloric curiosities.

The "Tree of Knowledge" in paradise with Adam and Eve. Woodcut from *Hortus sanitatis*. Augsburg, 1486.

The Pentagram: the five-pointed star is an
old symbol of health (SALUS). Woodcut from
the art-mythology *Imagini delli Dei de gl'An-
tichi* by Vicenzo Cartari, Venice, 1647 (reprint
Graz, 1963).

In many historical publications concerned with the origins of the art of healing, the metaphysical aspects of "Paleomedicine" are treated as a kind of "primeordial stupidity." According to the *Encyclopedia Britannica*, pharmacology up to the last century was primarily based on superstition, magic, religion and, at best, trial and error. The writer Thorwald, in a well-documented book about the "early physicians," is of the opinion that in the old Mesopotamia "rational remedies were seldom, if ever, free of magic, incantations and mysterious rites."

These irrational elements of the ancient art of healing are time and again—consciously and unconsciously—regarded as anti-rational and an obstacle to progress. Thus, it is tacitly assumed that today's prevailing logico-scientific way of thinking is the only one a reasonable person ought to concern himself with. With the aid of valuable manuscripts we will explore just how much magic and indications of the doctrine of "similars" or "signatures" are to be found in old writings on healing. In the process it will also become apparent whether a disparaging attitude toward a different way of reasoning and conception of the world is justifiable within the framework of general historical philosophy.

Undoubtedly the scientific healing methods of our culture permit us to effectively combat quite a number of diseases for which the priest-physician of earlier civilizations had no remedies. In this regard, however, we would like to raise the question of whether the complex and contradictory entity "man" can really be made healthier in every case relying solely on rational means. H. Sigerist, a medical historian, writing about the medical practices of old Egypt, considers the assumption erroneous. According to him, "The Egyptian medicine started off empirically, then developed toward the rational and finally degenerated to healing by prayer and incantation."

The ancient Hero or God of Medicine and Healing Asclepius (Aesculapius), from the Renaissance art-mythology by Vicenzo Cartari (see illustration on p. 8).

Sigerist questions the justification for a theory of retrogressive evolution since the sources are too fragmentary to fully warrant such an assumption. He believes that both kinds of healing efforts existed in tandem, the true medical and the sacerdotal.

But beyond that the question to be asked here is whether the medicine of prayer and incantation can solely be perceived as an abberation of rational healing methods. It could very well be that psychotherapeutic healing value can be attributed to it that cannot be found in the treatment of illnesses with only the aid of medication and causal working therapeutic methods. The human being of ancient cultures felt embedded in a large harmonious system of cosmic dimensions. He was ardent to uphold or to restore this equilibrium of the causative forces with means which to us appear largely unfounded, superstitious and absurd if we judge by our standard of thinking that seeks causal relationships based on logic. This will later on be more clearly set forth and, by way of examples, elucidated.

However, there is still extant a large void filled only with the art of healing. If that were not so, a country with a highly advanced modern medical science—perhaps the United States with its Mayo Clinic and innumerable other major hospitals which for our standards are fabulously equipped—should have the healthiest people.

But especially there seems to exist the need to go beyond the purely rational treatment limited to the physical aspect of the patient and tend him in other ways. Particularly here do psychotherapists of various persuasions have the most numerous help-seeking visitors. And not seldom do they appear to assume precisely that role of spiritual guide held long ago by the priestly practitioner of prayer and incantation healing methods: leading the patient to integral harmony and his proper place in the universe, a task which Medicine *sensu strictu* cannot accomplish. Medical therapy limited to the physical aspect, as perfect as it may be, does not

The Biblical account of the effect of the fruits of the Tree of Knowledge contributed to the great importance of the botanical world. Detail from Vol. VII of *Liber chronicarum* by H. Schedel, Nuremberg, 1493.

10

Another detail from the same woodcut pictured on the preceding page. The plant behind the mother of mankind, Eve, could be the dragon-palm of the Canary Islands.

seem to be able to do justice to the contradictory being "of two worlds." The fact that in the last decades psychosomatic medicine has received increasing attention demonstrates that it is not just a matter of influencing psychic disturbances and behavioral problems but goes beyond that to the physical well-being of the patient.

These deliberations would be purely theoretical if it were not possible by way of examples to support this just mentioned structure of "imbeddedness of human kind of archaic cultures" in a harmonious global oneness and the resulting integral therapeutical methods. It becomes necessary to undertake an excursion into the realm of anthropology since the history of medicine only rarely (e.g., H. Sigerist) draws on ethnographical parallels to clarify the ambiguity indicated.

The homeland of the Navaho nation, which today numbers about 100,000 people, is located in the southwest United States. It settled about 1000 A.D. in what is now the states of New Mexico, Arizona and Utah, and was culturally influenced by the local Pueblo tribes who lived in adobe dwellings. Its folk art is exceedingly charming and sophisticated and is based on a rich religious and mythical spirituality.The dances, rites and above all the healing ceremonies, of which various reporters give accounts, are likewise founded on the Navaho mythology. We are following here a treatise by A. H. and D. C. Leighton (*The Navaho Door: An Introduction to Navaho Life,* Cambridge, MA, 1966).

The object of the rites is to persuade the supernatural beings to intervene in the fate of the patient. These beings are those who roamed the earth in prehistoric times and retreated to the lands around the cardinal points (East, West, South, North, Zenith and Nadir) after they had created the Navaho people and had bequeathed to them the holy chants, dances and rites. Illness is attributed to a disturbance of the cosmic order. After the diagnosis is made, if the illness is judged too serious for the ability of a "healer of lower rank" rites are conducted, called the

"Blessing Way," which last about nine days and nights. Not only are sweat baths taken, as well as baths in a distillate of the Yucca root, but also the famous "sand paintings" are constructed with multi-colored sand. These are ephemeral drawings composed of fine textured earth colors spread on smooth ground to exact specifications and are part of the medicine man's secret legacy. Cosmic symbols, such as pictures of the large celestial bodies, the symbols of winds and the rainbow, and representations of the supernatural play an important role.

The afflicted is laid down in the center of these colorful cosmograms. After a while he feels the approach of the demons who made him ill—but this only happens if the sand paintings are truly faithful to the instructions that were handed down. The symbols then exert such coercive force on the spirits that they are unable to withdraw. The portrayals of the cosmic order put the spirits in a favorable mood and they are inclined to spare the sick person. If the sand painting is then erased with eagle feathers the demons have no more power and the patient feels purified and relieved.

These healing ceremonies with their incantations lasting for days and the banishment of the demonic beings are examples of genuine ritual magic within the confines of medicine. It is undoubtedly a fact that the believing participants experience a great emotional disturbance, and many experts concur in their opinion that healing can be accomplished as a consequence of these rituals. H. Sigerist writes, "Particularly the coherence of the primitive medicine, the fact that it never limits itself to either the body or the spirit but always considers both together, explains many of its successes even in the somatic domain. The fact that a ceremony, in the course of which a sick person attains complete harmony with nature and the universe, is of great psycho-therapeutical value is self evident."

The Finnish ethnographer Lauri Honko illustrates with numerous examples that in early cultures the person skilled in healing was not only

A schematic drawing of the cosmos and the guardians of the four regions of the world, from the pre-Columbian America (Codex Fejérváry-Mayer, Old-Mexico). Compare H. Biedermann, *Altmexikos heilige Bücher*, Graz, 1971.

Phol endruuodan uuorun ziholza duuuart
demobalderesuolon sinuuoz birenkic t
rhubiguolen sinhrguint · sunna crasuister
rhubiguolen fria uolla crasuister rhu
biguolen uuodansohr uuola conda
sosebenrenki soscbluotrenki sosclidi
renki ben zibrena bluot zibluoda
lid zugeliden sofegelimidasin ·

"Phol and Wodan went to cut wood . . ." So
begins one of the two Merseburger magic incantations recorded in the tenth century. Reciting the story of how long ago the gods
cured such an affliction with magic conjura-
tion was supposed to help cure a sprained
leg. This re-telling of a mythical event indicated the supernatural foundation of the
treatment and quite probably had a subjec-
tive healing effect on suggestible patients.

a physician but simultaneously priest, prophet, creator of myths "and beyond that technician, engineer and policeman. . ." He may not always have achieved lasting results, but in most instances he was able to guarantee the patient a temporary improvement. We can safely assume that he obtained the best results when he treated pathological disorders whose origins were psychical and behavioral. But could his psychotherapy have an effect on organic afflictions? This question must remain unanswered until medical science is in a position to define the "psychic factors" whose effect on tuberculosis, cancer, etc. are suspected today but not clarified. The surgeon E. Liek was of the opinion "that no breakdown in the living organism, no illness, whether we may call them functional or organic, are not to some extent receptive to psychological influences" (quoted from H. Vorwahl by E. Grabner, 1967).

The ethnologist Th. W. Danzel pointed out that in some cases both magical and rational healing methods fail, but that due to the high suggestibility of the people of early cultures an effective influence of the medicine man cannot be denied. It should be further noted, "that such ceremonies not only helped the sick person but often also his family," by "taking away the paralyzing fear caused by the sight of the terrifying symptoms of the illness." This experience may also have served as a verification of the magical and ritual healing methods. However, its primary function was to assure the patient, whose normal life had been disrupted, that after the treatment the natural order of his microcosm would be restored and would then mobilize the defense system of his organism.

Restoring harmony in the sick person is also the purpose of acupuncture, a healing method that has found a great number of followers in the Occident in the past years, despite the fact that it is not very comprehensible from the viewpoint of our scientific medicine and rests on a completely different theory. In its course needles are inserted into the skin of the patient in accordance with precisely established procedures.

13

Even if this unorthodox healing method may have at one time only served to expel demons, according to instructions recorded in the past, its purpose was to restore the proper flow of the primal forces of Yin and Yang and to harmonize the order in the microcosm of the human organism by stimulating the nerve tissues in proper places. Yin and Yang are antagonistic concepts whose effects can perhaps be envisioned by comparison to the effects of sympathicus and vagus in neurology. For us the study of foreign systems is important because here, as well as in Hippocratical medicine, harmony plays a significant role. Here also an effort is being made to prevent one force from becoming dominant and upsetting the natural equilibrium. Furthermore, we know from recent accounts that this concept, which completely deviates from our own, indeed "works."

It is important to mention one more example from the field of ethno-medicine, since it demonstrates that a dualistic physiological theory does not necessarily have to stem from the realm of an advanced civilization. Elizabeth Marshall Thomas, an American ethnologist, lived for an extended period with members of the remaining yellow-skinned Kalahari bushmen. She reported the prevalent notion that every person corresponded to a fundamental principle ("nau") of either "cold-damp" or "hot-dry." The effect would become evident if a person with a cold-damp "nau" scorched his hair at the campfire and as a result it rained or turned cold. A macrocosmic reaction to microcosmic occurrences is not being disputed. Despite the fact that this system is structured quite simply, it is nevertheless based on a very similar philosophy of corresponding theories found in early advanced civilizations. It is characteristic that no explanation could be given to the ethnologist when she asked for a logical explanation of the origin of the belief. "They do not know," reported Elizabeth Marshall about the bushmen, "how or why the 'nau' changes the weather, only that it does." This inability to formulate a cause and effect theory about these supernatural correlations is typical

The ancestors of the Kalahari bushmen, about whose idea of a bi-polar structured primal nature of the world E. Marshall Thomas wrote, left behind many impressive rock paintings in South Africa. The natural and supernatural often flow together: rock paintings from the Drakensberg range in Natal, beings with antelope heads above a rainbow (?), H. Pagen, Johannesburg.

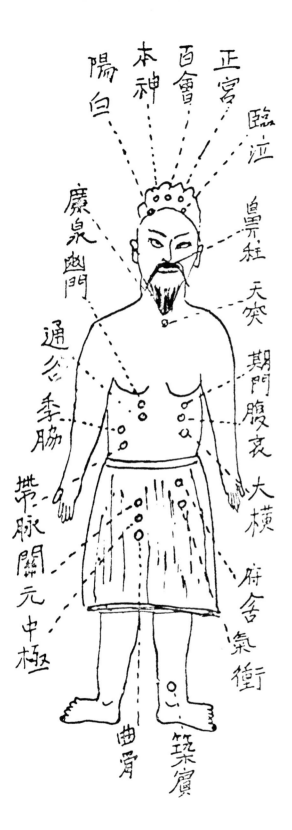

正宮
本神
百會
陽白
臨泣
鼻柱 天突
期門腹哀 大橫
府舍 氣衝
廉泉幽門
通谷 季脅
帶脈關元中極
曲骨
筑賓

for these people, though we may view their beliefs as irrational. It is therefore necessary to summarize clearly (p. 17 f.) what has already been touched on here and why a highly developed system of magic was part of the medicine of antiquity and was handed down over the centuries (regardless of the widespread opinion that Hippocrates had banished from the art of healing all things transcendental).

In this Chinese diagram the cosmic relationships between planets, "elements," the cardinal points, seasons, organs, qualities and divine symbols are established in the form of a pentagram. Danzel, 1924.

The purpose of the art of acupuncture, also practiced today in Europe, was to restore a harmonious condition between the primal forces of Yin and Yang through nerve stimulations.
◀ F. Hübotter, *Die chinesische Medizin*, Leipzig, 1929.

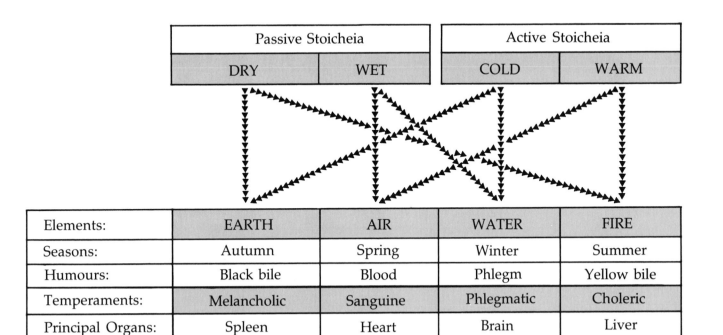

	Passive Stoicheia		Active Stoicheia	
	DRY	WET	COLD	WARM
Elements:	EARTH	AIR	WATER	FIRE
Seasons:	Autumn	Spring	Winter	Summer
Humours:	Black bile	Blood	Phlegm	Yellow bile
Temperaments:	Melancholic	Sanguine	Phlegmatic	Choleric
Principal Organs:	Spleen	Heart	Brain	Liver

A schematic illustration of the analogies and sympathies regarded effective by the Hippocratic, Galenic medicine, between the primal concepts, primal qualities, elements, seasons, humours (body fluids), the "four temperaments," and the organs of the human body controlled by them.

In the history of Occidental medicine the intellectual framework plays an important part. It reveals itself in the theory of the humours, the concept of the elements and the related sympathy doctrine, and is actually the touchstone of whether a certain aspect in the history of the art of healing belongs in an extended sense to the domain of "medicina magica" as it is the case with analogies or correspondencies.

While are are accustomed to using only valid causal relationships as the basis for scientific work, archaic logic can apparently do without such nexus and is satisfied with "as here, so there," without demanding a rational explanation. This "analogic" mentality lies at the root of most of the magic and mantic disciplines: the expert on the varied relationships felt capable of vitalizing and making them useful for his purposes. It is not always possible for us to perceive in a specific case the justification of this kind of parallel. Carl Gustav Jung introduced the term "synchronization" to describe a conception evolved from the notion of correspondency, i.e., the simultaneous occurrence of two or more events not causally connected or connectable. According to Jung, the simultaneousness leads to this kind of "hypothesis of acausal relationships" such as can be observed in astrology.

Such a theory dependent entirely upon a time concept is not quite enough to explain the desire to arrange wholly heterogeneous elements in a logical order and to structure the world *acausally,* and have it still be perceived as effective. While we are inclined to ask why and in what way the primal quality "wet" corresponds to the "element air," blood and spring, since we cannot perceive any relevant relationships or must first construe them with effort, such investigation is apparently irrelevant in the framework of a different mental structure. If we were not aware that intricate correspondence-tables, utilizing the archaic Stoicheia-Humour Theory, were still being prepared at the end of the eighteenth

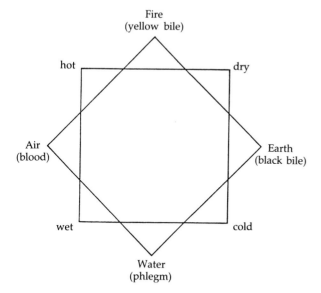

Picturing the Stoicheia-Somata-Schema in this way brings out its harmonious nature even more clearly.

century (e.g., Karl von Eckartshausens's book *Aufschlüsse zur Magie aus geprüften Erfahrungen*, Munich, 1788) we might arrive at the erroneous conclusion that acausal structuring was prevalent only in ancient cultures far removed in time. But in fact, it was actually an extremely important and frequently observed principle of systematization for many centuries, as the medieval *Tacuinum sanitatis* shows, from which we have reproduced some pages.

At first glance there does not seem to be anything magical or irrational about establishing precepts and indexes. However, we are dealing here with the kind of systematization that rests on ancient and pre-scientific correspondence theories. In the *Occulta Philosophia*, quite magnificent for its kind, Agrippa von Nettesheim groups angels, angel-choirs, evangelists, celestial bodies and elements and includes large correspondence indexes. The inclination to build systems is evidently a basic need of a thinking person because it is evident already in ancient, primitive communities. The Zuñi Indians of the south-western part of North America paired the North with War, the West with Hunting, the South with Agriculture and the Healing Art, and the East with Religion and Magic. Th.W. Danzel writes, "Safety and order rules all thought and deed of these people. There is never a celebration, a ceremony, a council meeting or procession where there could occur some kind of misunderstanding about the proper procedure, the position of the individual tribal groups, or the perogative that might be due to someone at individual activities. All this is so strictly defined by the system described, it not only equals written laws but surpasses them by far in its regulatory strength . . . The precepts are the beginnings of science for they (even if not logically) constitute indeed organized knowledge." It is the authentic ancient legacy of thought and perception of an earlier epoch that confronts us in the Analogy-Schemata based on the Humour theory.

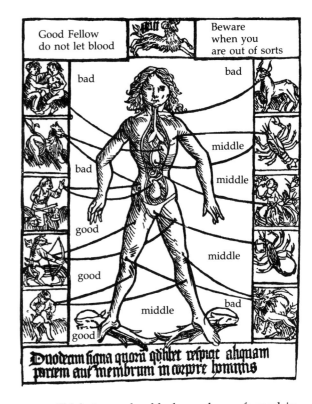

Phlebotomy should always be performed in harmony with the forces of the universe, whereby the position of the moon in a certain sign of the zodiac corresponding to a particular organ, was considered. "Phlebotomy manikin," around 1480.

18

The Humour theory originates from the Aristotelian doctrine of the four primal qualities (Stoicheia), namely "Cold" and "Warm", "Dry" and "Wet", from which, by combining corresponding pairs, the elements (Somata) result: Earth is derived from a combination of Dry and Cold, Fire by Dry and Warm. In the *Corpus Hippocraticum*, a collection of medical treatises connected with the name of the great Hippocrates of Kos (c. 460–375 B.C.), a book can be found about the nature of mankind (Perì phýsios anthrópou) that has been ascribed to a physician by the name of Polybos. Here the four humours of the human body are apparently mentioned for the first time, having evolved from earlier beliefs, and finally having been organized into a system.

Phlegm, bile and blood are already mentioned in earlier writings, as well as "black bile", evidently suggesting a cause for the dark discoloration of the stools of persons suffering from bleeding in the stomach-intestinal tract (e.g., stomach ulcers, stomach cancer, etc.) or that of the dark-colored urine by "blackwater fever." It seemed to have at first been the prevalent opinion that the normally yellowish bile ("A-bile," with bilirubin in today's concept!) breaks down and turns blackish ("B-bile," biliverdin) thus becoming a symptom of various illnesses. Also to mind comes the "pleiochrome" bile produced by Pernicious anemia and Hemolytic anemia.

However, in the book, *Über die Natur des Menschen*, "black bile" is upgraded to a normal fundamental component of the human body and is considered as one of the four cardinal humours which have to be mixed in the proper proportion for the human physis to be harmoniously structured. Consequently black bile is no longer considered a pathogenic essence but was apparently used to compliment the three already accepted humours to be able to reflect the quadruple nature of the elements of the human body. The theory of the four humours (fluids), phlegm, yellow bile, black bile, and blood, lives on in the popular names

Another depiction of the "Phlebotomy manikin," (from the *Martyrologium der Heiligen,* Strassburg, 1484).

19

for the "four temperaments" (phlegmatic, choleric, melancholic and sanguine), ostensibly indicating a dominance of the respective body fluids, but today's vernacular lacks the former assumption that the melancholics suffer from the "illness of the black bile afflicted."

The Swedish medical historian, Robin Fåhraeus, is of the opinion that the theory of the four humours found in the Hippocratic treatise on the nature of man originated from observations of drawn blood. After a time, due to the oxidation of the blood corpuscles, a light-red layer — "blood" in the proper and more specific sense — forms on its surface; underneath is the dark coagulated blood called black bile. After coagulation, the light blood serum — yellow bile — becomes visible. If the blood is being whipped before it congeals a yellowish-white substance, the fibrin, in Hippocratic terminology "phlegm," appears. The insights of this empirically derived classification were then secondarily linked with the philosophical theory of the Stoicheia and Somata. Regardless of whether theory or empiricism was in the foreground, a system was found that for many centuries was hardly ever questioned.

A kind of humour doctrine was prevalent in the Tibetan healing arts even in this century, as we learn from a study by Th. Burang-Illion. It espoused three primal essences, which the author compares to the "philosophical elements" of Paracelsus's alchemy (sal, sulphur, mercurius). "In a completely healthy person," so it states, "the three essences are in a well-balanced state of harmony. They stimulate and counterbalance each other. The 'phlegm' cools the 'bile', the 'bile' gives the 'phlegm' the proper warmth, and the 'air' slackens the other two essences without stimulating them excessively. The lack of harmony between the macrocosm and the microcosm in the human being can in itself be the cause for the development of an illness. One of the basic examples is the inadequate adjustment of people's diet to seasonal changes, which requires, for instance, an increased consumption of fruit in fall and use of fat adjusted to the time of the year, etc." We shall soon

	Symbol	Character	Correspondence
mercurius	☿	the "volatile"	spiritus
sulphur	♄	the "fiery"	anima
sal	⊖	the "tangible"	corpus

The three "philosophical elements" and their correspondences in the human sphere, according to the writings of Paracelsus and his disciples.

Temperament	Sanguineous	Phlegmaticus	Cholericus	Melancholicus
Element	Air	Water	Fire	Earth
Color	Brilliant and Luminary	White	Flame-colored	Lead-colored
Emotions	Levity and Mirth	Apathy and Indolence	Irascible and Anger	Sadness and Depression
Nerves	Easily Excitable	Torpid	Rigid and Dry	Weak
Fluids	Pure	Watery	Phlogistic	Thick and Viscous
Blood	Light-red	Watery and Albescent	Dark-red	Black
Circulation	Quick	Slow	Uneven and Forceful	Sluggish
Perceptions	Ephemeral	Apathetic	Quick and Spontaneous	Slow and Enduring
Modes	Dorian	Mixolydian	Aeolian	Lydian
Instrument	Violin, Oboe, Piano, Flute, Harp, Mandora, Clarinet	Organ, Bassoon, Alto-Viola, Bass, Lyre	Trumpete, Tympani, Drum, Cymbal, Zenelen	Trombone, Trompetes with Mutes, Violin with Mutes, Steel-Violin
Expression of Modes	Allegretto Amotoso Grazioso	Majestinoso Adantino Andante	Allegro Pianissimo Furioso	Adagio Largo

Correspondence plate of the "Sympathies" from the book Aufschlüsse zur Magie aus geprüften Erfahrungen *etc. by Karl von Eckartshausen, Munich, 1788, p. 381.*

become aquainted, by an actual example, with the fact that a very similar theory—with the one exception that in the Occident, four (instead of three, as in Tibet) humours were mentioned—served as the basis for dietary guidelines in Europe. The theory of the three primal essences which, prior to the introduction of the "black bile" to this system, seems to have been the most prevailing in Mediterranean regions, has in common with the Asiatic one "phlegm" and "bile"; the third element here is "blood", there "air."

We are accustomed to perceiving the humour pathology of, for example, the Middle Ages as a limited schematism which hindered the progress of medicine. In fact, the correspondence tables based on this precept can hardly be evaluated by rational standards. But we must not overlook the fact that here the basis was already a harmonic system of physical substances, not a method founded purely on philosophical theories of primal qualities and elements. The quaternion seems to indicate that Pythagorian speculations about the tetracties $(1+2+3+4=10)$ stood in the background of this design. Archaic, speculative and genuinely medical elements formed a quite impressive synthesis which, in the form of true therapeutical successes, apparently found confirmation to a certain degree, as shown by its having been proclaimed time and again even to modern times. It is conceivable that assuring the patient that his organism would again be in a harmonic order, comparable to the buildingblocks of the world after the physician's regulating influences on the irregularities, possessed a psychotherapeutic value that we today, having quite a different basis, can only realize with difficulty.

To illustrate how the theory of the humours has persisted over the years, let's listen to what the largest completed Encyclopedia of the German language, the *Universal-Lexicon* by Zedler, Volume 42 (1744, reprint, Graz, 1962) has to say under the guide-word "temperament." We understand "temperament of the body, Lat. *Temperamentum corporis,. . .* to be the blend of the various parts of which the blood of the human body consists . . . [Most] believe therefore that the entire substance consisting of liquid parts was a mixture of different and distinctive components, that each person's blood contained watery, oily and salty fragments, variously blended, causing differences in temperament and the predominance of one determines the category . . . Others ascribe air to the sanguinic temperament and water to the phlegmatic, concluding that fire, earth, air and water determine the temperaments. Thereafter, they probe the nature of the temperaments for the primary properties of the natural things or *primis qualitatibus*, according to which the choleric is warm and dry; the sanguinic warm and wet; the melancholic cold and dry; the phlegmatic cold and wet . . . The theory is presumed to be very old, Hippocrates having organized it, Aristotle having improved it and Galen having perfected it even further. From the latter still exists a manuscript, *quod mores animi temperamento corporis obsequantur*.''

We have selected only a short excerpt from the voluminous and detailed expositions which nevertheless illustrates the significance of the ancient theory of the Stoicheia, Somata, and the human types still relevant in modern times.

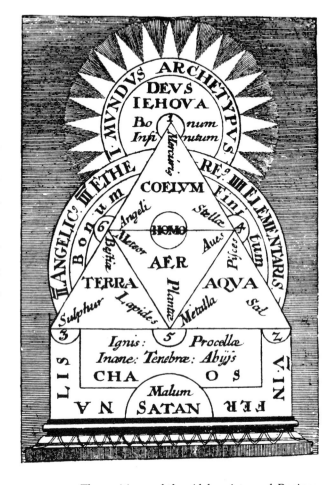

The writings of the Alchemists and Rosicrucians manifest time and again the effort to recognize harmonic universal concepts. World-schema from a treatise by the English alchemist Thomas Norton, which is contained in the collection ''Musaeum Hermeticum,'' *Frankfurt am Main* 1678 (reprint Graz 1970).

Being now familiar with the foregoing, we can recognize by use of a medieval example how the four fundamental types of people, also called "complexiones," were linked with substances of their environment to form a dietary formula for one's mode of life, and what practical dictates grew out of this tetramerous typology. We refer to the already mentioned manuscript originating from upper Italy, *Tacuinum sanitatis in medicina* (Cod. Vinob. ser. nov. 2644) written around 1390.

This attractively illuminated codex is based on the work of the Nestorio-Christian physician Ibn Botlan from Bagdad, actually Abu'l Hasan al Muhtar ibn al Hasan ibn 'Abdun ibn Sa'dūn ibn Butlān, known in the Occident under the bowdlerized name of "Abulcasis de Baldach" (in the Vienna manuscript, "Ellbochasim de baldach"). This healing expert—the year of his death has been established as 1064—wrote among other medical writings the *Tagwîm al-sihha*, i.e., "Tabular Summary of Health." In medieval Latin "Tagwîm" became the loanword "tacuinum," meaning synoptic table (in modern Italian "tacuino" means notebook). It is a correspondence-chart based on the antique Humour-pathology. It organizes 280 medicines, foods, animals, winds, kinds of water, seasons, and other environmental factors according to their effects on the four types of human kind, and describes their positive and negative influence. The *Encyclopedia of Islam* calls this work a "Synopsis of hygiene and macrobiotic in the form of a table" that was also widely taken notice of in the Occident. The Latin text came out in 1531 and 1533. The German version appeared in 1533 in Strassburg under the title of *Schachtafelen der Gesuntheyt* (health-tables), translated by Michael Herr.

For our *Tacuinum* the Arabian text served as a guide for the creation of a family edition which in colorful, brightly painted miniature illustrations describe the life of the common people and also in part that of the farmers at the beginning of the Renaissance. Parallel manuscripts ex-

The apothecary of the waning Middle Ages contained primarily drugs of herbal origin. An idealization of a council of masters of the art of healing. Woodcut from *Hortus sanitatis*, Augsburg 1486.

ist in Paris, Rome and Lüttich. The existence of two additional fifteenth century versions at the Austrian National Library illustrates how popular this topic was. The creators of these miniatures were not great artists, but especially the illustration of the genre scenes in our Vienna *Tacuinum* are distinct for their "fresh and bold realism." According to J. Schlosser, "Some of the pictures have a touch of buffoonery, even humor . . . In spite of the oriental background the depicted scenes of daily life as it takes place in all naturalness and without restraint, open for all to see, under open sky, in mild air . . . are quite Italian. One sees that this book of the Cerruti has the quality of a novella about it—not that of the courtly Decamerone, but of the Sacchetti narrations with their plebeian, somewhat ordinary milieu, which is of course characteristic for the second half of the Trecento."

The text gives a full account of all things in the human environment, as well as whether they possess prominent attributes in accordance with the Hippocratic theory concerning the Stoicheia Dry, Wet, Cold and Warm on a "scale" of one to three. Substances with a "cold and wet" complexion are beneficial for persons "with warm complexions," for example, a choleric, since they have a cooling effect and decrease an already existent, predisposed predominance of a particular body fluid instead of increasing it. "Aqua aliminoxa" (alum containing water), on the other hand, is "cold and dry and a three on the scale", and therefore recommended for persons "with warm and wet complexions" (therefore sanguinics). By "liquefying and checking of the fluids" a harmonious equilibrium is to be established, since the maintenance of health is based on the proper balance. Harmonic dietetic is also the basis for the recommendations of numerous drugs, foods and environmental factors with the help of animated genre-drawings. These are not only valuable records for the perpetuation of the humour theory in the Middle Ages but also anthropological documents of everyday life of the common people at the end of the fifteenth century.

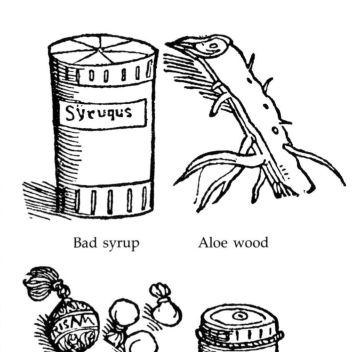

Bad syrup   Aloe wood

Balsam

Camphor

Woodcut from the book *Schachtafelen der Gesuntheyt* (health-tables) by Michael Herr, based on the *Tacuinum sanitatis* (1533).

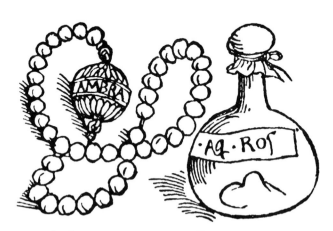

Ambergrist   Rosewater

Sour syrup

Ambergrist, rosewater and syrup acetosum
from the *Schachtafelen der Gesuntheyt*.

In the framework of the iconography in the table section, the accompanying Latin text can only be reproduced by way of suggestion. The structure of the text is governed by the schema a) "complexio" (i.e., base-type according to the Stoicheia-theory), the effectiveness indicated by degrees; b) "electio," likewise a listing of the qualities of a substance in question which are especially valuable; c) "juvamentum," benefits to health; d) "nocumentum," detriments to health; e) "remotio nocumenti," remedies for the prevention or cure of the defect; f) "quid generat," something like, "the respective substance causes . . . in a human being" (e.g., phlegmatic blood); g) "convenit," "it is beneficial for . . ." These reoccurring passages attest to the original headings of the overview tables. To be sure, "the categories which are appropriate for food and its evaluation cannot be used very well for seasons, winds, human activities and dispositions. Therefore this rigid schema seems sometimes analogous to the bed of Procrustes, to which all things must adapt. Nevertheless, suggestions and evaluations are often to be found, that to this day are generally accepted and adhered to" (H. Unterkircher in the commentary of the complete facsimile edition, Graz, 1967).

Thus the same is true for our *Tacuinum* as Diepgen wrote about a similar text, the "Regimen sanitatis salernitanum," a poem about health written about 1300. It was soon translated into the then existing languages and augmented by many additions: "German texts of it existed already in the late Middle Ages. As a science, this health guide is long outdated in most aspects. As folk-medicine, it lives on today, outlining the theory of the four temperaments, the ideas about the particular lifestyle one has to keep if one is a phlegmatic or sanguinic, a melancholic or cholic, and the regimen of sleep and activity, food and drink."

The medico-historical significance of these suggestions can only be well appraised when the principles of these teachings of the quaternately arranged correspondence scheme and the pursuit of microcosmic harmony are known. For physicians who follow a purely empirical and modern scientific path this schema is not adequate. For them the "Galenic theoreticians," with their essentially analogistic/magic basis, were by nature a bone of contention. Out of this conflict of the ways of reasoning and procedures arose modern medicine. In regard to its empirical basis and its techniques, it is vastly superior to the "medicina antiqua." Para-rational elements become apparent only by careful inspection. The realization of greater inter-relations (beyond treating specific illnesses and deficiencies) has been lost to a great extent not only by medical science but by humanity in general. We may smile conceitedly about cautious attempts at universality with the aid of ancient analogy schemata. But by objective consideration we have to admit that here are ancient wisdoms and insights hidden—at times in a strange form—which we can only re-discover if we can learn to rid ourselves of any illusions of superiority based on our progresses.

Theophrast of Hohenheim, called Paracelsus (1493–1541), battled against the school-medicine of his day and did not hesitate to acquire from uneducated, simple people the fundamentals of natural living and the use of healing herbs.

A detail from the great herbal by the controversial alchemist Leonhard Thurneisser, *Historia sive descriptio plantarum omnium*, Berlin, 1578. In this work the author tried to tie the effects of drugs to astrology. This picture is part of "Foenicula mare, quod alias Hippomarathron vocatur."

Strictly speaking, herbals are not really part of medical literature. But since the Pharmacopoeia of Paracelsus's time consisted mainly of herbal medicines, the physician must have at least a general knowledge of the officinal herbs. In antiquity, primarily the herb-gatherers and root-diggers (Rhizotomoi) concerned themselves with the procurement of this most important fount for medicine. In the Middle Ages the Biblical word in the proverb of Sirach was highly regarded. It says: "The Lord lets the herbs grow out of the soil, and a wise person does not scorn them." Physicians and pharmacists perceived these words as an instruction to pay heed to the medical herbs.

Until modern times the sources for most pharmacological books were Greco-Byzantine manuscripts. Since pharmacology has its origins among the herb-gatherers, it is obvious that many features of folk-medicine crept in, as well as beliefs about the effects of the drug that a physician savant would hardly have advocated. For example, herbs are mentioned which supposedly protect from bewitchery, which—when carried as amulets—renders one sterile or leads to the procreation of male offsprings. The healing art arising from these old herbals is often marked by folk-magic features even though empirically obtained, genuine knowledge surely prevails. Irrational notions from popular beliefs are frequently combined with medically ascertainable effects of alkaloids. This is also not seldom the case in the "primitive medicine" of exotic tribes where one can often find herbal draughts which in some form are slightly narcotic or work in some other verifiable way as drugs. However, this alone does not explain their true therapeutic value. The psychological impact of the healing ceremony must be added for the combined treatment of medicine and suggestion to be effective. In modern times, faith in the healing capacity of specific drugs has been proven very powerfully in "placebo" experiments. Gerhard Venzmer once

27

pointed out, "that there are relatively few illnesses for which a purely medicamentary effect—free of any 'irrational components'—can be claimed." (*Eingebildete Heilmittelwirkungen. Der Zauber der Arznei.* KOSMOS 6/1957).

The solanaceous mandrake (the mandragora is its anthropomorphous root) is an example of this kind of medicinal plant. Its picture can be found in almost all medical and drug-related manuscripts. It is open to question whether this is more of a magic drug or a pharmacologically valuable medicine in the modern sense. On one hand it has been proven that the ball-shaped fruit of the *Mandragora officinalis* contains the alkaloids hyoscyamine and scopolamine and has an anesthetizing effect. Therefore, giving an extract of the mandrake fruit during a difficult birth is a "sensible" measure. However, if, on the other hand, the bizarrely formed, forked and ramified root-stalk—the mandragora—is dressed up and kept as a charm for good luck or wealth, we are no longer dealing in the realm of medical history but in popular beliefs or superstition. This was by no means limited to the rural population but played a part in the highest social circles. Originally the root-diggers probably paid more attention to the root of the night-shade plant than to its fruit. And many literary passages lead us to conclude that the "male" (Norion) and the "female" (Thridacias) mandragoras were thought of as aphrodisiacs. According to legend, they grow under the gallows from the sperm of the hanged and are therefore *homunculi* from the plant-world. The digging-up of these mysterious shapes were accompanied by special ceremonies.

Josephus Flavius (A.D. 37–93) mentions in his *Judischen Krieg* (VII, 6,3) a plant—which certainly seems to be the mandrake—whose roots try to resist the root-digger and that anyone who nevertheless uncovers it will die. For this reason a dog, who subsequently perishes as a substitute sacrifice, is used to pull it out of the soil. This "Baara" root, according to the author named above, drives away the hostile demons. Earlier, the Greek philosopher Theophrastus (approx. 370–287 B.C.) in his books

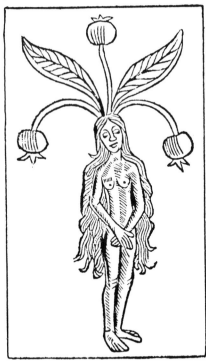

Mandrake in male and female form, from the *Hortus sanitatis* by Johannes de Cuba, approx. 1498.

28

on botany had written about some particular ceremonies which were observed by the herb-gatherers when they unearthed the roots. Claudius Aelianus (A.D. 170–235) described it as a remedy for epilepsy and eye-ailments. During the Middle Ages Hildegard von Bingen (1098–1179), among others, writes about this plant and is of the opinion that in it the influence of the devil is more perceptible that in others and that its effect incites good as well as evil. In Shakespeare's *Romeo and Juliet* there is reference to the blood-curdling scream that the root supposedly utters when it is pulled out of the earth. Many books about drugs advised that this terrible, life-threatening sound can be drowned out by blowing the trumpet and stuffing one's ears. In the novel *Isabella von Agypten* by Achim von Arnim, this whole concept is made vivid. The medical manuscripts pictured in this volume depict not only the male and female mandragora drawn according to their name "Anthromorphon, Semihominis, Hominiformis" but also the dog who pulls it out of the sheltering subterrestial abode into the light of day.

In our time the pharmacological effectiveness of the root is quite often discussed and mostly disputed. Above all, the prevalent belief of the aphrodisiac effect of the root is scientifically not justified. It is conceivable that the medicinal properties of the fruit of the mandrake (probably identical with the "dudaim" in the Bible, the love-apple mentioned in the Song of Solomon) were discovered by coincidence. Perhaps during their digging the herb-gatherers came upon the root-stalk that with some imagination resembles a human form and as a result it became increasingly more important than the fruit until it was more significant in the realm of superstition than as a medicinal plant for the pharmacopoeia. But the reverse is more likely—that the human form of the root-stalk induced the herb-gatherers to experiment with the plant for healing purposes. If this is so, the ancient belief of the "Signatures" would indeed be significant. According to this idea, the healing herbs, by virtue of their configuration, show the attentive observer for what purpose

Two mandrake plants from the *Codex neapolitanus,* written about A.D. 700, supplem. gr. 26 of the Bibliotheca Nazionale in Naples. The mandrake pictures of the *Wiener Dioskurides* probably looked similar.

29

they want to be used: heliotrope perhaps as a remedy for bites from venomous animals, because its blossoms are shaped like "scorpions"; or the bryony for dropsy since it resembles a swollen human leg.

The doctrine of the Signatures, still highly regarded by Paracelsus and later physicians, pre-supposes a supernatural (divine) design of healing. According to this view, nature is created for mankind who is destined to unravel the codes of the plant kingdom for his benefit. Here again the reasoning is not based on cause, but on analogy. The perceived correspondence is substantiated by the similarity in form. Zedler, in his *Universal-Lexicon* (1743), regards the doctrine of Signatures as a guide "to the particular similarity of specific herbs and other substances with the parts of the human body or its afflictions and should therefore be regarded as beneficial for such parts or as salutory for such afflictions." The heart-shaped leaves of the balm and wood-sorrel are to indicate that these plants are a remedy for heart ailments. In 1622, Jakob Böhme wrote that every object has its mouth for the purpose of revelation and "this is the inate language by which each thing speaks through its particular characteristics and constantly reveals for what it is good and useful." In this context, the "human form" of the mandragora was to be perceived as a supernatural insignia and indication that this plant is highly important for humankind.

In view of the significance as "medicina magica" given to healing drugs based on beliefs passed down from antiquity, such as the *Codex 93* in the Austrian National Library, K.A. Nowotny in his commentary on the great Agrippa von Nettesheim edition (Graz, 1967) raises the following points: The plant itself is document of a myth or, by its existence and form, proof of a mythical event (e.g., it grew from spilled blood); perhaps its importance for the healing art was recognized—as it is mentioned in many legends—when animals were observed regaining their health or renewed youth when eating this plant; the plant might be a gift to mankind from supernatural beings (gods, heros, half-gods); per-

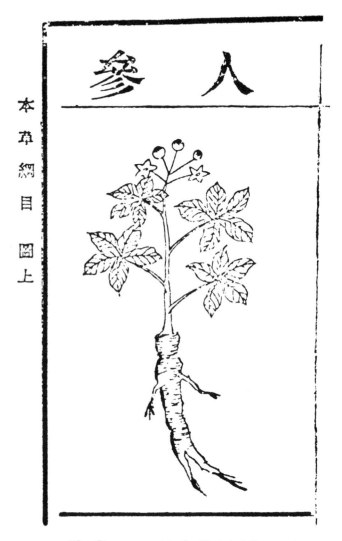

The Ginseng-root is the East Asiatic counterpart of the mandrake. It contains vitamins, volatile oils and glycoside as active ingredients. From a Chinese reference book on healing-herbs, *Pen Tsao Kang Mu* (1597).

30

haps it shows by a "signature" of color and form for what purpose mankind, for whom it was created, should use it.

Myths play an important part in herbals, as shown by information passed down in handwritten manuscripts. But in more recent publications they fall more and more in the background (Brunfels, Bock, Fuchs, Gesner, Cordus, *et al.*). Therefore, these manuscripts on healing drugs are valued records of thought and perception which otherwise have been passed down to us only in legends. Ancient forerunners of such medieval codices are especially the herbals of Crateuas, physician to Mithridates VI (120-63 B.C.), and of Pedanius Dioskurides, who was army surgeon at the time of Emperor Claudius (10 B.C.-A.D. 54). Whereas Crateuas's pharmacological work with its descriptions of plants was alphabetically arranged, Dioskurides tried for a relevant classification of his remedies and a guide to various states of growth and maturation.

This collection of information was highly respected for a long time and praised by Galen as the most complete of its kind. Translated into Latin, alphabetized and supplemented from other sources, it was reproduced many times in the Middle Ages as *Dyascorides*. The early pharmacological books consisted most likely solely of text and the plants had to be elaborately described. But soon the need arose to depict the various herbs with the help of illustrations. In the beginning the drawings were done according to living plants or pressed specimens. These illustrations are remarkable for their true-to-life quality. In the Middle Ages other motives moved to the foreground, which are incompatible with the modern study of nature. New aspects gained more importance than "temporal substances." The best minds of this epoch did not seek bodily health but eternal life.

From a scientific point of view, the early period of the Middle Ages may justifiably be called the "Dark Age." But to deduce a general value judgement from this designation attests to an inadequate criterion.

The first pages of the *Wiener Dioskurides* show figurative drawings; one of them is reprinted in color in the plate section (Plate 25), another one is shown here in the form of a redrawing from Lambeck's *Commentarium de Augustissima Bibliotheca Caesarea Vindobonensis*, Vienna 1680.

Whatever the case may be, during that time the drawings of the various plants were often copied from each other. It is therefore not surprising that the true-to-life quality suffered increasingly. This was especially apparent in drawings of plants that were only native to the region of the Mediterranean and do not grow north of the Alps. Only some of the herbs listed on drug charts by the physicians of Salerno could be grown in Middle Europe.

If we compare the Byzantine *Anicia-Juliana-Codex* (the sixth century A.D. *Wiener Dioskurides*) with the thirteenth century *Codex 93*, the life-like quality of the drawings clearly declines. However, the medieval *Codex* with its rich, figurative illustrations is of great folkloric importance: the pages come alive with dramatic scenes of fights with poisonous animals, mythical animals and mythological creatures such as centaurs and genies surrounded by bizarre caricatures. Purely artistically and from the viewpoint of illustrative quality, the way from the *Wiener Dioskurides* to the *Libri IIII medicin(a)e (Cod. Vind. 93)* collection from the thirteenth century should rightly be called a degeneration—an impression that an impartial viewer of the drawings of both manuscripts can hardly avoid. Only if serious consideration is given to the differences in the guiding principles of the two worlds from which the codices stem, can one do justice to the later manuscript.

Let us take a brief look at these two pharmacological sources, both valuable in their own right, as was done earlier with the Vienna *Tacuinum sanitatis*.

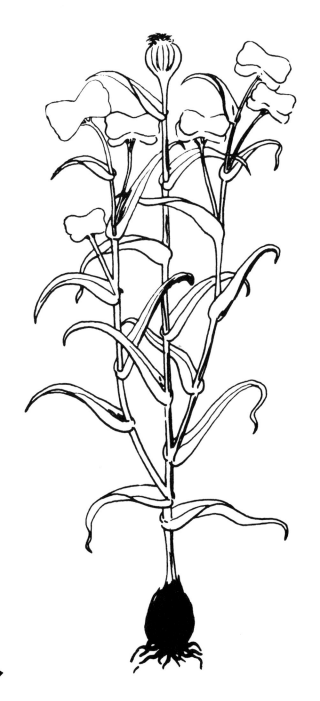

Allium Moly, Allium Dioscoridis, Allium magicum or Allium nigrum: a facsimile of a drawing from the *Dioskurides-Bildes* on fol. 234 verso, showing the fabled herb, "Moly". It points out the difficulty in the botanical identification of some plant illustrations. The picture shows big, brownish blossoms, but the text describes it as whitish and smaller than the blossoms of a violet. It is quite apparent that the illustrator did not know what the plant really looked like (compare Plate 20).

The *Codex 93* in the Austrian National Library is a collection of transcripts of handwritings from antiquity. It contains a large number of manuscripts of the same genre, including treatises and essays by men skilled in the art of healing, such as "Antonius Musa," "Lucius Apuleius," "Sextus Placidus Papiriensis" and "(Pseudo)-Dioskurides." All of the original texts were written in the first centuries A.D. This work, however, is outstanding for its beautiful illustrations of artists' conceptions of the author, mythological scenes, pictures of cities, scenes of medical treatments, animals, ornamental forms, more recent pen-and-ink drawings and drawings of little figures pointing out important text passages. This codex is therefore an inexhaustible storehouse of information of the history of civilization. And at the same time it presents a graphic account of the acceptances and changes of the ancient ideas and thoughts during the Middle Ages.

The immediate forerunner to which the artists of this codex did not, of course, have access, dates back to the sixth century A.D. and was repeatedly copied. One of these copies was the source for the *Codex Vind. 93*. In addition, scenes on antique mosaics and votive reliefs might also have served as references. Guided by the type (miniscule of the Ital. Gothic) and the details of the native costumes of the people (bonnets with ribbons of the Staufen period), it can be fairly well established that the manuscript under discussion originated around the middle of the thirteenth century in Sicily. Even though some of the embellishments seem a little barbaric, this is offset by the bold and artless design and beautiful colors. In the manuscripts of the later Middle Ages this is often displaced by a frilly and stilted style. Heavily represented are healing methods of pagan origins (conjurations, magical incantations, mythical scenes) from the late antiquity. Here and there, out of Christian fervour, someone has erased those, for him, embarrassing traces of the antiquated beliefs, as has been done with the genitalia of most of the nudely depicted persons.

The doctrine of the "Signatures" of the plant kingdom played an important role in early and medieval medicine; the Italian scholar Giambattista della Porta (1540–1615) attempted to depict the "Sympathies" that link plant and animals by their morphological features.

In the original book the foremost thought was that the health of mankind was determined not only by external factors but also by supernatural influences—perhaps by the benevolence of gods and genies who are being invoked on the two full-page miniatures "precatio terrae" and "precatio herbarum." The Christian physician agreed in principle, only for him the grace of God took the place of the pagan gods. In this way, the antique text with its numerous examples of the early healing beliefs could endure and was only superficially moralized by elimination of invocations to the genies of the healing herbs or by keeping secret the contraceptive substances. It is important to note that during that time the belief about the transcendental foundation of health and illness remained untouched. Christendom added only some new aspects. The belief that Aristolochia (birth-wort) will ward off "demoniacos incursiones" was not disputed with the argument of the inexistence of such demons of pagan times, but a pen-and-ink drawing in the margin shows a horned, claw-footed devil coming out of the "possessed" woman and the small pointing figure is not just carrying a stick in his hand, but a cross.

Even though this manuscript is not a great work of art from the artistic point of view, it nevertheless is of special importance because of its unique position in regard to human thinking and perception in the historical framework (late-antique healing beliefs in a Christian environment). This becomes fully apparent only if one is willing to submerge into the world of thought of a physician of the Middle Ages working with antique knowledge. At this time, independent, empirical observation occupied an insignificant place and gained strength only later when the brilliant Frederick II, Emperor of the Hohenstauffen line, wrote his *De arte venandi cum avibus*, a book about falcons (also published in facsimile). However, the manuscript with which we will concern ourselves next—the oldest and most valuable—will give us an idea of what the archetypes of the simple drawings of plants in the *Codex 93* looked like.

34

WHITE DITTANY · *Dictamnus albus*

Fraxinella · 86

in distress I call on you.
Dittany is beneficial and strengthening not only renowned for external use but also internally. There is no distress whether from the outside or the inside that you cannot escape with God's protection.

A drawing of a plant from the baroque *Lust- und Arzeneygarten deB Königlichen Propheten Davids* by W.H. Freiherr von Hohberg (Regensburg 1675): Dittany (*Dictamnus albus*). The botanical drawing is supplemented by moralistic sayings.

A monument built at the beginning of the sixth century is without a doubt of respectable age. Much more surprising is a book of such an age, since books are normally much more exposed to destructive environmental factors and the ravages of time than a building made of stone, and especially since this particular book has been passed from hand to hand and has been in use every day by physicians for a whole millennium.

The *Wiener Dioskurides*, an illustrated Byzantine herbal, is one of the greatest and oldest books in existence. It is a priceless work of gigantic proportions, with magnificent drawings of plants from late antiquity. In comparison, later examples of this kind appear crude and unskillful.

The pharmacological collection of Pedanios Dioskurides (c. 60 A.D.), based on earlier works of Crateuas and Mithridates VI Eupator, possessed the greatest authority during the entire Middle Ages which continued into the modern era, not only in the East-Roman region with its Greek features but also throughout the Latin cultures of the West. The main text of the *Dioskurides* is organized according to subjects: 1) spices, oils, ointments, trees; 2) animals and animal products, grains and pot-herbs; 3-4) healing herbs and roots; and 5) beverages and minerals. However, the *Wiener Dioskurides-Codex* uses again the older alphabetical classification of the Materia medica. Each plant picture is supplemented with texts from Dioskurides, Crateuas and Galen and the variations of the particular plant names primarily according to Pamphilos. This manuscript, venerable not just for its age, was written prior to the year 512 in Constantinople. It had been commissioned by the people of Honoratae (Pera) for the Princess Anicia Juliana as a gesture of appreciation for her gift of a church.

The reason the people of Honoratae chose to present the princess with this beautifully adorned herbal may have been the then fashionable

Dittany (Diktam(n)on), copy of a plant picture from the *Wiener Dioskurides*, fol. 99 *(Organum dictamnus)*.

35

bibliophilistic tendency among the ladies. On the other hand, H. Gerstinger, in his commentary in the complete facsimile edition of the manuscript, maintains that the content of the book might have been of practical interest to the princess because of the medical dilettantism practiced in her circles. "Perhaps the fact that particularly the mandrake is shown on the two pictures of the author (fol. 4 and 5) might indicate a special interest of the recipient in this magic root." It has to be added, that the mandrake was the most clearly "human-signified" plant and therefore almost a symbol for the medicina magica; this is certainly enough justification for the important role it plays in the illustrations of all three of the codices which we have introduced in this book.

Besides the substantial, illustrated herbal section, the *Wiener Anicia-Juliana Codex* contains other medico-pharmacological treatises in the back of the book but these are of lesser importance. The principal value lies in the large pictures of the plants. It is possible that these are copies of earlier originals from the third century A.D. Nevertheless, they are not soul-less imitations but, for the most part, genuine works of art. They give us an idea just how high the level of the art of book-illustration must have been in the Hellenistic Alexandria. Evidently, this model was not a book in the modern sense but rather a book-scroll.

Paging through the codex or the facsimile reproductions, the reader becomes aware at once of at least two large, distinct groups of pictures in regard to conception, style and delineation. The first group consists of the beautiful plant-portraits of fol. 12 verso to 42 verso *et al.*, and also the pictures of asphodel, plantain and portulaca. This group of pictures was probably drawn using life plants as a guide. They seem well proportioned, plastic, and have a natural quality in spite of a certain stylization in an effort to achieve spacial harmony. According to H. Gerstinger, one can speak of a naturalistic portrayal by artistically excellent trained painters as far as this is possible in the framework of scientific illustrations

Copy of the picture of fol. 280 recto, labeled as "Periklymenon" (i.e., *Lonicera etrusca*, honeysuckle). However, the picture shown is without a doubt the bear- or corn-bind, *Convolvulus arvensis*.

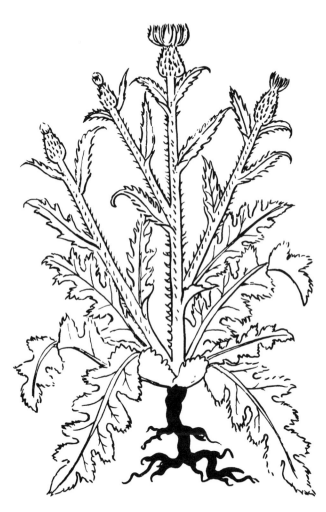

Copy of the plant picture of fol. 53 verso: *Acanthos agria,* spiny Acanthus. Here we have a drawing of that group of pictures that appear "flat and schematic" in contrast to the one on the opposite page.

restricted by the purposes of the herbal. The pictures of the other group are quite different—they lack depth, are rather schematic, more severe in their symmetric composition, and their colors are not as vivid. Therefore the reviewers concluded that these pictures were drawn according to dried and pressed specimens, not live plants. The fact that some of these pictures, for example the Akanthus drawings of fol. 51 verso to 53 verso, are characterized only by such attributes as "plain, flat, not very natural," is a somewhat one-sided evaluation, using strictly life-like quality as criterion if one considers the high graphic quality and the firm and energetic delineation. However, differences in quality exist within both groups.

Inasmuch as the purely graphic quality of a leaf is less consequential than its true-to-nature likeness for the purpose of this book, it is understandable that the botanist and pharmacologist evaluate it exclusively by the criterion. Depending upon the category of the illustrations being contemplated, the critical assessment is either positive or negative. Van Swieten, Haller and Sibthorp were convinced of the pharmacological value of the illustrations, whereas Clusius, Jacquin, Sprengel and others judged them rather negatively. There are indeed drawings that do not quite live up to the natural forms, "some are clearly freely contrived" (H. Gerstinger). However, this fact should not lead to the conclusion that all picture herbals from antiquity bear these features. The *Anicia-Juliana-Codex* was not—as we have pointed out—compiled for a scientific purpose but rather for the use of a princess who dabbled in pharmacology. This may be the reason that the artist did not feel the need for exactness. It is conceivable that some of these pictures were simply drawn from memory if a real picture of a hard-to-find herbal plant was not available for a model. This may explain why a botanist occasionally has difficulties cataloging the *Dioskurides* illustrations scientifically, using the modern nomenclature. The "Séseli peloponnesiakón" on fol. 330

verso could be either the hogweed *(Lophotaenia aura)* or the sweet cicely *(Myrrhis odorata)*. In most cases, however, the identification is possible without too much difficulty, and the true-to-lifeness is usually combined with high artistic quality.

The plates were much sought after, so much so, that as a result the codex is no longer complete. For example, the two mandrake pictures, probably of special interest in this codex, were already cut out (after fol. 226) before the Middle Ages. Three smaller pages were bound-in in another place (fol. 287 to 289) in antique-looking Greek writing from the thirteenth century and contain a transcript of the missing text of the "peri mandragora" and a small mandrake drawing. It is of course not a very satisfactory substitute for plates which art connoisseurs found before the priceless value of this manuscript was realized.

We must remember that in our age of antibiotics it is difficult to imagine the awe that people of earlier centuries felt when dealing with healing plants (or such considered as healing). Each name reveals the magic these plants once had for the herbalist: "crowfoot, Euphorbia filled with caustic fire, the hen-bane, the belladonna, fox-glove of them poison-mixing queens and veiled cleopatras, growing in untilled glens and cool forests. To continue, the camomile, the kindly sister with her thousand smiling bonnets, serving the healing drink in an earthen bowl; the pimpernel and the sickle-wart; the peppermint . . . naming them all is like reciting a shepherd's poem full of grace and light . . . precious healing plants and sweet-smelling herbs: sage, tarragon, fennel, thyme, now all of them old maid-servants deemed no longer useful and receiving here their bread of charity out of tenacious tradition." So writes the poet Maurice Maeterlinck in his book *Der doppelte Garten* (1920) about plants that also appear in the herbal of Dioskurides. It is good to recall such sentiments; the purely scientific assessment of these precious pictures will not suffice if one is to understand what the artists wanted to express and indicate in these drawings of the materia medica!

Panax Herakleios, today called *Ferula Opopanax* or *Opopanax hispidus* (Giant Fennel). Copy of the plant picture from the *Dioskurides*, fol. 281.

38

The healing plant as the source of active ingredients plays only a minor part in our pharmacopoeia. Therefore, we know their value only from folk medicine. However, it is not unthinkable that some day certain concentrations of active and ballast substances that appear in some healing plants will receive more attention than they do today.

MINT · Mentha · 112

For the devout the light goes on in the darkness
The mint is a salutory little plant and it is advisable to have it always on hand:
So also is piety, like a seed that yields good cheer and strength. Happy is he who practices it.

The mint is a salutory little plant . . . Plant picture from Hohberg's *Arzeneygarten* (see p. 34).

Angel-choirs	Seraphim Cherubim Throni	Dominations Potestates Virtutes	Principatus Arch angeli Augeli	Innocents Martyrs Confessors
Angels as Guardians of the Cardinal points	Michael	Raphael	Gabriel	Uriel
Guardians of the Elements	Seraph	Cherub	Tharsis	Ariel
Evangelists	Mark	John	Matthew	Luke
Planets	Mars Sun	Jupiter Venus	Saturn Mercury	Fixed Stars Luna
Elements	Fire	Air	Water	Earth

One of the many Correspondence tables from the *Occulta Philosophia* by Henricus Cornelius Agrippa ab Nettesheym. It is based on analogical principles and revitalizes antique thought in the time of humanism. It orders the world and the world beyond with all its manifestations of divinity into a harmonically structured whole.

From the store of manuscripts relevant to medical history we can present examples of only three codices in the form of pictures characteristic for their origin and prevailing thought. Facsimiles will be shown that constitute not only valuable reference material in the more restricted framework of medical history but also in the wider sense of anthropology and philosophy. In this compilation we have also included a discussion of the theories of analogy as an outgrowth of the "medicina magica," for example the correspondence system in the *Tacuinum sanitatis*, based on the four humour theory which is not usually considered in this context. It was necessary to include this material because we are dealing with vestiges of pre- or rather para-causal reasoning pointing to earlier epochs of beliefs and perceptions in spite of the seemingly scientific approach.

The desire to restore the balance of a faltering system of fundamental elements, i.e., to bring about harmony, is in itself not primitive, but timeless. Even physicians have time and again concerned themselves with the theories of harmony. In the works of the English Rosicrucian, Robert Fludd, (Robertus Fluctibus, 1574-1637), we find not only clear anatomical drawings but also large instructional tables, establishing the dominance of cosmic harmony in the microcosm of the human organism. Especially the proportions of the intervals, which he interprets as harmonizing number relations, play an important role in his teachings. Endeavors of this kind are by no means isolated instances from the history of medicine but are of interest in our own time as well. Rudolf Haase is such an example. In his book, *Geschichte des harmonikalen Pythagoreismus*, he refers to the physician Hans Weier's experiments, which were inspired by the harmony-research of Hans Kayser, (1891-1964): "Conducting for many years his clinical experiments with high-frequency radiation and finally by using two particular frequencies that

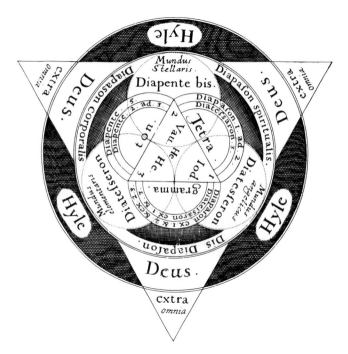

Meditation picture, depicting number relations as an expression of divine world harmony on the background of unformed matter (Hyle). From the book, *De supernaturali, naturali, praeternaturali et contranaturali micrososmi historia*, etc., Oppenheim 1619, by the English Theosophist and Rosicrucian, Robert Fludd, 1574-1637.

41

formed a musical interval, he achieved remarkable healing results. From these experiments he developed his bioscillator-theory and constructed a suitable instrument which is now also being used by other physicians with good results." Perhaps this constitutes a starting point for the utilization of old, time-honored beliefs in the framework of the modern art of healing as it is done in a different sense in the Yin and Yang harmonizing acupuncture.

The striving for cosmic harmony in the small world of the human organism, the knowledge of psycho-physical interrelations, the sporadic emergence of mythical elements from pre-Christian times—these were the principal aspects that we encountered on our voyage of discovery into the "medicina magica" of bygone centuries and millennia. Mentioning archaic thought structure does not constitute an evaluative point of view. Paralogism is frequently evident in modern thought, though we seldom acknowledge it. Whether a philosophy based purely on reason is closer to objective truth than one primarily analogistic cannot be answered *a priori*. It is not the purpose of this book to provide answers to fundamental questions of historical thought, but to encourage questions and, with the help of a selection of plates from ancient manuscripts on the art of healing, to take a look into the depth of the still largely unexplored being, "mankind." This being today, just as countless millennia ago, battles against the dark shadows of sickness and death which threaten his existence.

Meditation picture: the wonders of nature in the center of the symbols for the planets and metals, surrounded by the "four elements" and the signs of the zodiac.
From the alchemistic collection, "Musaeum Hermeticum", Frankfurt 1677 (1678) (compare p. 22).

A. THE FACSIMILE EDITIONS OF THE CODICES

A list of the complete facsimile editions from which excerpts were taken for this book.

TACUINUM SANITATIS IN MEDICINA (Codex Vindobonensis S.N. 2644). Graz 1966. Vollständige Faksimile-Ausgabe der 214 Seiten (107 Blatt) des Codex im Originalformat 230 × 330 mm. 206 ganzseitige Miniaturen, 2 Seiten Wappen. — Kommentarband: Graz 1967. Vorwort von Generaldirektor em. DDr. J. Stummvoll; Einführung, Transkription des lateinischen Textes und deutsche Übersetzung der Bildtexte Dir. em. DDr. F. Unterkircher; englische Übersetzung der Bildtexte H. Saxer, Wien, und Ch. H. Talbot, London. (Vol. 6 der Reihe ,,Codices Selecti'').

MEDICINA ANTIQUA (Libri IIII medicine, Codex Vindobonensis 93). Graz 1972. Vollständige Faksimile-Ausgabe der 322 Seiten (161 Blatt) im Originalformat 186 × 275 mm. — Kommentarband: Graz 1972. Kodikologische Beschreibung von Dir. em. DDr. F. Unterkircher; medizinhistorischer Kommentar von Ch. H. Talbot, London. (Vol. 27 der Reihe ,,Codices Selecti'').

DER WIENER DIOSKURIDES (Codex Vindobonensis Med. gr. 1). Graz 1965-1970. Vollständige Faksimile-Ausgabe der 984 Seiten (492 Blatt) im Originalformat 310 × 380 mm. 392 ganzseitige und 87 in den Text eingefügte Bilder. — Kommentarband: Graz 1970. Wissenschaftliche Bearbeitung von Prof. em. Dr. H. Gerstinger, Graz. (Vol. 12 der Reihe ,,Codices Selecti'').

B. LITERARY REFERENCES

Ackerknecht, Erwin A.: Kurze Geschichte der Medizin, Stuttgart 1959.
Agrippa ab Nettesheym, Henricus Cornelius: De Occulta Philosophia.

Nachdruck der Ausgabe Köln 1533, kommentiert und herausgegeben von Karl Anton Nowotny, Graz 1967.

Berendes, J.: Des Pedanios Dioskurides Arzneimittellehre in 5 Büchern, übersetzt und mit Erklärungen versehen von J. B., Stuttgart 1902.

Biedermann, Hans: Handlexikon der magischen Künste von der Spätantike bis zum 19. Jahrhundert, Graz 1968.

Burang, Theodor: Tibetische Heilkunde, Zürich 1957.

Danzel, Th. W.: Magie und Geheimwissenschaft in ihrer Bedeutung für Kultur und Kulturgeschichte, Stuttgart 1924.

Diepgen, Paul: Geschichte der Medizin, Bd. 1 — Von den Anfängen der Medizin bis zur Mitte des 18. Jahrhunderts, Berlin 1949.

Encyclopaedia of Islam, The — New ed. by B. Lewis, V. L. Ménage, Ch. Pellat and J. Schacht, vol. III, Leiden-London 1971.

Fåhraeus, Robin: Grundlegende Fakten über die Pathologie der Körpersäfte und ihre Relikte in Sprache und Volksmedizin (1962-63). Bei Grabner (s.d.).

Flashar, Hellmut: Ant. Medizin. Wege der Forschung CCXXI, Darmstadt 1971.

Gordon, Benjamin Lee: Medicine throughout Antiquity, Philadelphia 1949.

Grabner, Elfriede (Hrsg.): Volksmedizin. Probleme und Forschungsgeschichte. Wege der Forschung LXIII, Darmstadt 1967.

Gunther, Robert T.: The Greek Herbal of Dioscorides . . . englished by John Goddyer A.D. 1655, ed. and first printed A.D. 1933, New York 1959.

Haase, Rudolf: Geschichte des harmonikalen Pythagoreismus. Publikationen der Wiener Musikakademie, Bd. 3, Wien 1969.

(Hohberg, W. H. Freiherr von): Lust- und Arzeneygarten des Königlichen Propheten Davids. Nachdruck der Ausgabe Regensburg 1675, Einführung und Index von G. Lesky („Instrumentaria Artium" Bd. 8), Graz 1969.

*The Lord is righteous in his ways
The centaury, disagreeable because of its
bitter taste, nevertheless helps every
time: In the same way God treats us
harshly but all comes out well to his
glory and praise.*

(After Hohberg)

OREGANO · *Origanum* · 54

I will make you a thank-offering
The little oregano plant has a strong
mysterious effect, it freshens the blood,
it is good for the spleen and the lungs:
Therefore if God helps us and lets it
grow well, we should make a thank-
offering.

(*After Hohberg*)

Honko, Lauri: Über die tatsächliche Wirkung der Volksmedizin (1962-63). Bei Grabner (s.d.).

Hoppe, Heinz A.: Drogenkunde, Hamburg 1943.

Hovorka O. v. und A. Kronfeld: Vergleichende Volksmedizin, Stuttgart 1908-1909.

MacKinney, L.: Medical Illustrations in Medieval Manuscripts. Wellcome Hist. Med. Library, London / Berkeley 1965.

Marshall Thomas, Elizabeth: Meine Freunde, die Buschmänner. Bei den Nomaden der Kalahari. Berlin 1959. Engl. Originalausgabe: The harmless people, New York.

Möse, J. R.: Volkstümliche Pflanzenheilkunde im Lichte moderner Antibiotikaforschung (1958). Bei Grabner (s.d.).

Most, Georg Friedrich: Encyclopädie der gesammten Volksmedicin, oder Lexicon der vorzüglichsten und wirksamsten Haus- und Volksarzneimittel aller Länder, Leipzig 1843.

Müri, Walter: Melancholie und schwarze Galle (1953). Bei Flashar (s.d.).

Nissen, Claus: Die botanische Buchillustration, ihre Geschichte und Bibliographie, Stuttgart 1951.

Sigerist, Henry E.: Anfänge der Medizin. Von der primitiven und archaischen Medizin bis zum Goldenen Zeitalter in Griechenland. Vorwort E. H. Ackerknecht, Zürich 1963. Engl. Originalausgabe: A History of Medicine, Oxford.

Venzmer, Gerhard: Fünftausend Jahre Medizin, Bremen 1968.

Vorwahl, Heinrich: Deutsche Volksmedizin in Vergangenheit und Gegenwart (1939). Bei Grabner (s.d.).

Wrigth, Harry B.: Zauberer und Medizinmänner. Augenzeugenberichte von seltsamen Heilmethoden und ihren Wirkungen auf primitive Menschen, Zürich 1958.

Zedler, Johann Heinrich (Hrsg.): Großes vollständiges Universal-Lexikon aller Wissenschaften und Künste, 68 Bde., Leipzig und Halle 1732-1754, Nachdruck Graz 1961-1964.

Drawing of the mandrake from the *Herbarius zu teutsch*, Augsburg 1488.

FACSIMILE — PLATES

PLATE 1

Tacuinum sanitatis, fol. 4 recto

The first page of the miniature section in the *Hausbuches der Cerruti* from Verona, which is so named after a coat of arms, shows the learned physician speaking to his pupils. It seems to be the artist's idealized conception of Ibn Botlan, called "Ellbochasim de baldach" (Abu'l Hasan from Baghdad). The artist portrays a professor, typical of his country and his time, perhaps modeling him after the famous physicians of Salerno. These medieval healers have an air of dignity and confidence about them—the charlatans in their academic gowns which Paracelsus so vehemently fought in his battle against conventions must have looked just like them.

The title of the text begins with the words "Tacuinum sanitatis in medicina, ad narrandum sex res necessarias": health chart for medical problems dealing with six essential topics. They contain the advice of the best experts of the antiquity on the benefits and the negative effects of food, drink and clothing.

Following is a list of these six factors: the air that goes to the heart (qui cor conti(n)git); the preparation of food and drink; the regimen of activity and rest; the safeguards of the body against excessive sleep or wakefulness; the proper treatment of the body humours of either laxation or constriction (rectificatio laxationis et constrictionis humorum); lastly the personal discipline (regulatio) for prudence in happiness, anger, anxiety and fear. Health lies in the proper balance (equaliate) of these factors. The aim is to advise what is best for each individual according to his type of constitution *(secundum complexionem)* and his age, without superfluous talk and without mentioning conflicting opinions of the savants: people want only help from the experts, not explanations and definitions! Therefore, it should all be presented precisely and well organized with God's help.

This is not a highly scientific work but one aimed at dietary practices. The *Tacuinum* does not contain literary records of scholastic debates, but rather guidelines for the lay-person, interested in medicine.

Tacuini sanitatis i medicina. ad narandū sex res nēcias. unariatice uiuāiti cibori ⁊ potuū.
⁊ idumtorum nocumīti ipiuz. Et i rēmotiōe nocumitorum uix ōscilia meliorū erantiquis.

Tacuinū sanitatis de sex reb; q sunt nēce cuilib; ho̅i ad cotidiana ō suatiōe; sāitatis sue eiͥ
sius recti fiet opatioīb;. Pͥima ē sͥpatio aeris/qui cor: contingit. ⸪Scḋa rectificatio

Citonia. ꝙ plo. fri. ꝉ ſic. mᵒ. Electiō ꝙpleta gꝛoſſa. uuiani. letificat ꝛ ꝙfoꝛtat apetitū. nocumē̄
cauſāt colica. Remᵒ nocti cū dactil melius. Quid gn̄at huioꝛe; fri. ꝛueniut mag coliꝯ
.omni etati. omni. tp̄. omni regioni.

PLATE 2

Tacuinum sanitatis, fol. 8 recto

Citonia, quinces, are the subject of this plate, which is characteristic for most of the botanical miniatures of the book. Not only is the plant being presented, but also the people. A young man in court attire and two elegant ladies, all three in pointed shoes, pick quinces and enjoy their fragrance.

The text points out that the quinces, by their nature, are "cold and dry in the second degree." The biggest and the fullest are the best. They are beneficial for the heart and stimulate the appetite, but can also cause colic. But this can be avoided by eating sweet dates. Quinces produce "cold humours." For this reason they are especially beneficial for cholerics (since they cool and have a harmonizing effect). One should eat them throughout the year and in any region.

51

PLATE 3

Melones dulces, watermelons: a farmer in a simple, belted coat is cutting watermelons and putting them in a round basket. The leaves on the vines are drawn in a simple style in order to decorate and fill in the picture.

The explanatory text describes the nature of watermelons to be cold in the second- and wet in the third degree. The best ones come from Samarkand (this remark is an indication of the oriental origin of the text), especially the ripe, firm fruits with good color and aroma. They are effective in dissolving stones and for cleansing the skin. However, they can cause diarrhea *(fluxum ventri),* though that can be prevented by taking oxymel. Watermelons enhance the building of blood and are particularly recommended for the phlegmatic and the choleric as well as for the young and old. They are the best in autumn and at summer's end, and in regions with a temperate climate.

Melones dulces. qplo. fria. in 2. humida in 3. Electo. samara candi 7 maturi bone sic co-
loris 7 odoris. iuuamtum frangut lapide. 7 mundificat cutis. nocumitu. puocat fluxum
uentris. Remoto nocumiti. cu. syr. acetoso. Quid giuant sanguie; moicuz queiunt flec'
7 colicis. etati. scili. uuuenili. autipno. 7 fine estatis 7 regionib; tepatis.

Cucurbite. 2plo. fri ⁊ hu̅. l. i ꝰ. Gectio recêtes unitas. uuam̅tum̅ mitigant. sitim. No
cumitum. citô lubꝛicant. Remio nocum̅ti. cui mu̅ri ⁊ sinapi. Quid gn̅at? nutrimtꝛ
modicu̅ ⁊ friꝰ. ꝗuenuit colicis uuem̅bꝛ estate. om̅ibꝛ regioibꝛ ⁊ pᷓpue mꝺioᷤnalibꝛ.

PLATE 4

Tacuinum sanitatis, fol. 22 verso

Cucurbit(a)e, bottle-gourds: the artistic style is reminiscent of the watermelon drawing. Here, too, the vines are taller than the people since part of the ground is seen from a bird's-eye view. A farmer, similarly dressed as the melon picker, and a graceful lady, perhaps his mistress, examine the ripe gourds and put them in the round basket.

The accompanying text describes the bottle-gourds as cold and wet in the second degree. The best ones are green and fresh. They quench the thirst and work rather quickly as a laxative. But this can be prevented with saltwater and mustard. For the body, they are light and cold food because of their coolness and moisture. They are good for the choleric and the hot-blooded youth. They are good in summer in all regions, especially southern countries.

PLATE 5

Tacuinum sanitatis, fol. 40 recto

Fructus mandragor(a)e, mandrake fruit. The picture shows a strange scene: a root digger is about to flee, and a plant with a human-like root is partially pulled out of the ground by a black-and-white spotted dog, who is drinking water from a bowl. Folk tradition can explain this scene which the painter was not quite able to do because of the nature of the activity: since the magical mandrake root emits an ear-splitting scream which could kill a careless herbalist, a dog, whose life is therewith sacrificed, must do this task. The root cutter puts a rope around the dog's neck, attaches the rope to the mandrake and puts drinking water at some distance. When the dog runs toward the water he pulls the mandrake out of the ground.

According to Ibn Botlan, the mandrake fruits are cold in the third and dry in the second degree. The best of its kind are the large and fragrant fruits. Inhaling their scent protects against feverish headaches and insomnia. A poultice prepared from it helps against insomnia and skin infections. They do dull the senses but that can be rectified with ivy-berries. The mandrake fruits are not edible; they are salutory for the hot-tempered, the young. One should use them in summer and in southern regions.

Other (older) mandrake pictures are shown on Plates 23 and 25 of this book.

56

fructus mandragore. qplo. fri. iij. sic. i ?. Electo magni odorifer. uuiam. odorado itra soch̄
calam̄. 7 uigilias. emplando elefantie 7 ifectioib; nigris cutis. nocuui. electat sensus Re
noctī. cū fructu edere. Quid guāt nō e comestibile huenit. ca. iuieib; estate 7 mediauis.

Autumpn̄. ꝙplo. frī. t̄pate mr̄. Electo̅ meduſ ıp̄ı. uıuẽnı. g̅datū. pbez̄; ad̅ꝫꝫıa. ut ad calıdū̄
ṭhu̅ ſuccū̄. nocet t̄patıſ ꝙplombz̄; ꞇ dıſpoⁿ ad ptyſız̄. Remıo noctı cū̄ huẽctãtıbz̄; ꞇ balneo. Od̅
auget buoꝛeſ melecolıcoꝛ ꝶueıt. ea. ꞇhu̅. uıuẽmıbz̄; ſıue aꞇo̅l eſeetıbz̄. ea. ꞇhu̅. regıoıbz̄; al̅ t̄patıſ.

PLATE 6

Tacuinum sanitatis, fol. 54 verso

Autumpnus, autumn. After the botanical pictures follow some that deal with cultural themes; first two from the cycle of the four seasons: autumn at the time of grape harvest. The high stemmed grape vines climb up on trees and poles. The grapes are brought to the winepress and tread with the feet. All three people, including the woman, wear simple clothes. The fresh fruit juice is being collected in a wooden tub.

However the subject of the text is not the wine but autumn, which is rated as "temperately cold in the second degree." The best part of autumn is the middle. It is most favorable when the climate is gradually changing and no abrupt weather changes take place. It is detrimental for people with a "temperate constitution" (complexio) and those with an inclination to consumption. Full baths and sponge baths are preventive measures.

Autumn increases the melancholic humour but it is beneficial for people of the "warm and wet" type because of its temperately cold nature. Some believe it is good for young people and in humid regions; others believe it to be good in temperate zones.

PLATE 7

Tacuinum sanitatis, fol. 55 recto

Hyemps (hiems), winter. Here again we have a genre-scene before us, this time the interior of a house. The outside wall of the house has been left out. The old man in red dress sitting by the open fireplace under the smoke flue is tending the fire. A young woman with pinned-up braids lets hot air under her dress which she has gathered up rather indecently. This causes the young man who carries in firewood to laugh. As we know, an open fireplace only warms the immediate area of a room. The gnarled root that the young man is bringing will probably serve to sustain the fire for the night.

According to the scholarly text, winter is normally cold in the third degree and wet in the second degree. The best part of winter is the end of it. It is good for gallbladder diseases (also for feverish illnesses) and it strengthens digestion. But because of its cold-wet nature it is harmful since it increases the phlegm for those whose stoicheia is also cold and wet. Fire and warm clothing are recommended to prevent such harm. Winter is beneficial for people, whose nature is "warm and dry", for the young and for the inhabitants of southern and maritime regions.

60

hyemps. ꝗꝑlo. fꝛi. iꞡ. ꝑu. iꞡ. maliꝰ ſe hꝰ. Electo finiꝰ ei. uuuauꝛitum eꝗtuduniꝫ. oliciꝼ et
ꝗfoꝛtat diꝺoneꝫ. noꝛum. noꝛet eꝗtuduniꝫ flatitiꝰ ꝛauget ſla. Remo noꝛti eu igne 7 ueſtimuꝛ
Conuelit. ca.ꝛ.ſi eꝰ. uuenuꝫ. mꝛdiauꝼ 7 mautmuꝼ ꝛegiounꝫ.

Canes leporie. 2plo. ca.7.sic ur. Electo Juniores capti. puenatores canes. uiua. 2ferunt supa —
tis amulta pinguedie. Accuintuum uigilare fatuit. Remo nocuiti ci aroma aromatibz sb'
tiliatiuis. Quio gñant humore melecoliru. 2ueiunt mag.fris. decrepitis. hyeme 7.fris. te

PLATE 8

Tacuinum sanitatis, fol. 72 recto

Carnes leporine, rabbit meat. This picture of a coursing-hunt is a true specimen of naive nature presentation. Here again the elevated perspective is noticeable. The countryside is seen as from a tower with the horizon almost touching the top of the page. The animals in the background seem out of proportion in comparison to the minutely drawn leaves and grasses.

Greyhounds with collars and pointers without collars chase two rabbits. One of them seems to look back fearfully. Two beaters in colorful clothing and soft soled leather shoes talk animatedly about the results of the hunt.

According to the text, rabbit meat is warm and dry in the second degree. Best is that of young animals who were caught by hunting dogs. It is good for those suffering from obesity, but it can cause insomnia (the rabbit is a vigilant animal and sleeps with open eyes, according to popular belief and this peculiarity may be transmitted to the consumer of its meat!). But this can be avoided by adding aromatic and enhancing substances. Rabbit meat forms the melancholic fluids. Since it is "warm and dry" it must be good for people with a cold nature, for asthenia and in winter in northern regions.

(Compare the hunting scene from the *Medicina antiqua,* Plate 21!)

PLATE 9

Tacuinum sanitatis, fol. 74 recto

Carnes uachine (vaccinae) *et camelorum,* cow and camel meat. The oriental Ibn Botlan wrote among
other topics about the benefit of camel meat. Therefore the artist of the miniature had no choice
but to include this, to him, exotic animal in his illustration of a butcher's store. The three customers pictured in the lower right hand corner seem equally surprised. The stage-like look of the
room does not seem quite as strange since it could be an open-air store.

   According to the description, cow and camel meat are (as is rabbit meat) warm and dry in
the second degree. The meat from young animals, who are used to labour, is to be preferred.
For this reason it is thought to be good for working people (here again the thought prevails that
the quality of the meat could be transmitted to the eater). It is also good for those suffering from
an overflow of bile *(patientibus fluxum colericum).* It can (like rabbit meat) create melancholic fluids, such as heavy melancholic blood. This can be remedied with sugar and pepper. The author's
opinion here is—actually contrary to the normal schema—that it is good for persons with a warm
constitution and for the young. Also—and this agrees again with the customary effort towards
balance—that it should be eaten in winter and in northern regions.

Carnes uacce 7 camellozum. ꝯplo. ca. 7 ſic. inᵈ. Electo uuenum excitatiaᵣ. uuiam, pſtant
excitantibʒ; ſe 7 pacientibʒ fluxum colicum. Nocuuntum fatuit egrudimbʒ melicolicis. Rem.
nocuunti. cum. ꝫ. 7 piꝑ. Quio gñant ſanguiné groſſum melecolici. Conuemunt magᵉ caˢ
uuuiribʒ; venᵉ 7 ſeptentrionalibʒ :·—

Cerebra, spto. fri. 7 hu. m2. Electo ex animali spleto. uuam. adusti cerebruz 7 cor ipignat.
Nocumtum tarde digistur giant fastidium ato corrumpnt. Remo noeti cu sale origano pule-
gio montano spebz. ca. 7 sbtiliatiuus. Quid giant sanguine; flaticum uiscosum. Couenint
mag. ca. uuuembz. byeme. 7 fris. reqionibz.

PLATE 10

Tacuinum sanitatis, fol. 77 recto

Cerebra animalium, animal brains. Here again a butcher shop or rather a butcher's market-stand is shown. Two well dressed gentlemen have stopped by. The butcher is turning toward them while on the left a shabbily dressed farmer with an empty basket must wait until the customers, from whom a higher profit can be expected, are taken care of. A spotted dog scavenges for discarded scraps of meat.

Ibn Botlan classifies brains as cold and wet in the second degree. The best is that of a fully grown animal. It increases the brain and is fattening but difficult to digest. It can be repugnant and spoils rather quickly. This can be prevented by adding spices: salt, oregano, mountain flea-bane *(pulegium montanum),* and warm and refined additives. Being a "cold and wet" substance, brain builds phlegmatic, thick blood. It is recommended for hot-tempered people and the young. Further—and this contradicts the schema but is explainable by the fact that it spoils quickly!—it is recommended in winter and in cold regions.

PLATE 11

Tacuinum sanitatis, fol. 80 verso

Splenes, spleen. This miniature shows the kitchen of a late-medieval middle-class house. It has an open fireplace, a smoke flue, the kettle is suspended on the chain, the grill and a wall niche serving as a cupboard. A kitchen boy turns the spit and holds a raw spleen in his hand. A cook in red dress is in charge of preparing the roasted pieces. The artist of this miniature was apparently not entirely familiar with the pitfalls of perspective, because the table stands along the back wall and the cook seems to be jammed flat between the wall and the table.

The word splenes is preserved in the English "spleen" and the text says that the spleen generates viscous and melancholic humours. It is warm and dry in the second or first degree (the author seems to have had difficulty here with the system). The best spleen is that from young and fat animals, particularly from pigs. It strengthens the constitution and the effect of the body humours. It is not recommended for people suffering from melancholy but ill effects can be prevented by the intake of fat and much oil. It is good, however, for people with "warm and wet" constitution factors (therefore for the sanguine), for the young and the people of mountainous regions, especially in winter.

Splenes. ◌plo. ca.2.sic. in 2. al. p. Electo ex pingnibꝫ alibꝫ ⁊ innenibꝫ ⁊ pᶜipue pozcozum.
uniamitum adignoss̄andum ◌plone; ⁊ buozes. nocumitum patientibꝫ melencoliā. Remō
nocumiti cum pinguediē ⁊ oleo mlͭto. Quid gñant buozes malum ⁊ melēcolic̄ ꝗuenuit

Lampte oplo fri. 7 hu. i ƺ. mdo:is tñ hu. qͥ anguile. Electo fluis occurtis sup petras. uuia.
impinguat 7 multum nutriunt. Nocuint um sto debili 7 huic Remo nocuimti ei salunitis
7 pipe. Quid gñant humo:e flegmatieu: ɔueniunt mag. cal. 7 sic. iuuenibꝫ autipno 7 estate

PLATE 12

Tacuinum sanitatis, fol. 84 recto

Lamprete, lamprey. After several interiors we have another outdoor scene, fishing for lamprey with the net. A fisherman, his doublet pulled up, is standing in the water trying to get the lamprey out of the current with the net. The catch is kept in a wooden casket and a buyer has arrived who will carry the live animal home in a jar. Here, as in other drawings of landscapes, it is noteworthy that the background is not filled in with blue sky but rather "empty space."

Lampreys, according to the author, are cold and wet in the second degree though not quite as wet as eels. One should get them from a river that flows over a stone bed. They are fattening and very nourishing. But they do not agree with a "weak and wet stomach" *(stomacho debili et humido)* and therefore salt and pepper should be added (pepper is a "hot" spice). They are recommended for people with a "warm-dry" constitution (for cholerics), since they generate phlegmatic humours, for the young, in fall and summer and they can be better digested in northern regions.

PLATE 13

Tacuinum sanitatis, fol. 90 recto

Nix et glacies, ice and snow. A rather imaginary landscape is shown here —it is quite evident that the painter of this picture either had never seen a mountain region with his own eyes or he deliberately meant to draw a bizarre form. A donkey with a rather long neck carries wood fastened onto his back by some sort of primitive saddle pack. His driver, wearing a fur cap, is prodding him with a stick. Even though the pictured scene seems a somewhat strange landscape, its bold delineations have strong graphic quality.

Ice and snow, advises the author, are cold and wet in the third degree. Both are salutary if they come from good fresh-water. They improve digestion, but cause coughing, though that can be avoided if one drinks a small amount before eating the ice and snow. Ice and snow also cause pains in the joints and paralysis but are good for people with a "warm constitution." Also they are good for the young and, in order to compensate, especially good in summer in southern regions.

72

Nix ⁊ glacies. Complo. fri ⁊ hu̅. iiᵒ. Electo eraqua dulci ⁊ bona. uuuan̅. melioꝛat digo-
nem. Nocuimtum tussim ꝓbuet. Remo nocti bixedo antea mochcū. Quid g̅iiat uestica
tioneꝫ uictizazuꝫ ⁊ palustin. Conuenit mag. cā. uuuinbꝫ. estate mexoianis regioibꝫ.

Camere byemales. ⁊ plo. debet ee tpate. icali. Electo que assilant exteutati ius. uiua
excitat utuites sopitas er frr. acus. Nocumitum indueit sitim. ⁊ fatuut descede cibu
crudum. Remo nocti cu dispone usus aere septentrioale; Couert mag̃ frr̃is. decrepitis

PLATE 14

Tacuinum sanitatis, fol. 97 verso

Camere hyemales, winter-dwellings. After we have become acquainted with domestic life in winter (*Hyemps,* fol. 55 recto) we now see two more wood carriers in front of a middle-class house—a one-story building with a flat roof and a dove-tailed battlement stands before us. The main section of the house with its twin-arched windows appears smaller than the entrance, an indication of the artist's struggle with perspective. It seems to be a scene in early winter, since the fruit tree in the background is still bearing fruit. The servants, carrying the firewood from the wood-pile into the house, wear caps and pointed hats. The knees of the leggings have been mended.

Winter dwellings should be moderately warm. The air should be of the quality as that of the air at the end of the spring. The mild warmth awakens the energy grown sluggish by the cold air. The atmosphere in the rooms during wintertime makes individuals thirsty and leaves their food undigested. To prevent this, the rooms used in the wintertime should face north. The warm room temperature is good for people with a cold constitution (melancholic and phlegmatic), for weakened people, on very cold days in the mountains. The author cautions about overheating the room during the winter.

PLATE 15

Tacuinum sanitatis, fol. 100 verso

Confabulator, the conversationalist. This cozy scene by the open fire is the last of the manuscripts
we selected to illustrate the dietetics based on the analogical principles of Ibn Botlan. The old
man, dressed in red, is strongly reminiscent of the one pictured in the winter-scene (fol. 55
recto). A woman is sitting across from him holding a distaff (at the time few spinning-wheels
existed and were not generally in use; the earliest picture of this utensil comes from the house-
book of the Waldburg-family about 1480). A young man and two children have also gathered
around the flickering fire in order to listen to the stories of the bearded man who seem to make
them sleepy.

   Ibn Botlan seems to have had such discussions in mind when he wrote that conversation
by its very nature is one of the main causes of sleep. It is good for the person desiring to go to
sleep, says the author, if his partner in conversation is congenial. If someone is cheered by the
story, it not only improves the state of mind and spirit but also the digestion! However, it is
harmful if several people talk simultaneously if one wants to listen to only one. It is therefore a
good idea to ask those one does not want to listen to to be quiet. Conversation is good for all
types of people, and for all ages with the exception of children. It is good at all times of the year,
but especially in winter and in populated regions (the author probably feels that it is easier there
to find someone suitable to talk to who has a relaxing and soothing effect).

Confabulatio nra. e. una cir sompni. Electo ucies ne uolctis dormir. uuim. delectatib; ipa.
meliorat i eq oigones 7 sens 7 sps. Nocumtum audur ples cofabulatores. cu uoluit n uni. audic.

PLATE 16

Medicina antiqua, fol. 9 recto (alt 33 recto)

The *Codex Vindobonensis 93* consists of several tractates and is richly illustrated. It is an extremely interesting example of the continuation of antique traditions in the Middle Ages. This picture is near the beginning of the *Codex*. It illustrates a 51-line invocation: the "pr(a)ecatio terrae", invocation to the divine Mother Earth.

The picture is divided into horizontal zones. The lowest shows the realm of water with a river-god sitting on an imaginary fish. On the bank of the river the solemn adjuration to the Mother Earth, who rests on a large snake and holds in her hand a cornucopia, takes place. Behind and next to her plants are sprouting up that are the primary object of the prayer.

"Hoc quod peto a te, diva, mihi presta volens/herbas quascumque generat tua maiestas/salutis causa tribuis cunctis gentibus/Hanc mihi permittas medicinam tuam/veniant mecum tuis virtutibus . . ."

On the back-side of the original of this page, where this invocation can be found, the reader will be able to find some of the lines only partially. In the Middle Ages a devout reader of this book took offence on some of the pagan chants and scratched out words and made corrections with ink. The first line in the original "Dea sancta Tellus, rerum nature(a)e parens" (Divine Goddess Earth, who brings forth all things of nature) became "Deo santo" (To the divine God). However, a manuscript exists in Florence that was not tampered with, which made a reconstruction of the text possible. An additional invocation, "precatio herbarum," can be found on the picture fol. 12 recto in the codex (text on 13 recto). In this one the healing herbs themselves are being implored to bestow to one the health contained in them. In the late antiquity, the time when the prototype of this codex originated, it was quite clear to the physician that besides the effects of the drugs, immaterial factors had to be taken into consideration if healing was to result.

PLATE 17

Medicina antiqua, fol. 32 verso

Fol. 32 of this codex shows a rather awkwardly drawn plant-picture depicting one of the artemisia plants. A more artistically painted example of this plant from the Byzantine codex of the *Wiener Dioskurides* shall be featured later on. The painter of the codex pictured here endowed this plant mistakenly with camomile blossoms.

However, we are looking at the back side of the page, at the illustration of *Artemisia leptafillos* since here the mythological origins of the art of healing becomes apparent. The centaur Chiron stands before us with his robe blowing in the wind. In front of him a bearded man (perhaps Aesculapius or the mythical author of this book?) holding the healing plants in his hand—in the right hand the sage-brush, in the left hand the incorrectly portrayed ragweed *(Botrys artemisia)* which received through a mistake by the artist lily blossoms. Both plants are mythologically linked with the goddess Artemis. The text above the scene states that all three kinds of the Artemisia plants have been discovered by Diana and were then given to mankind by the benevolent centaur Chiron.

This picture and all of the following up to the artist's conception of Dioskurides are taken from the section of the codex that contains the "pictorial herbal of the Pseudo-Apuleius Platonicus." Who this Apuleius was is not clear. Perhaps it is a description of Peleus, a descendent of the centaur Chiron, who is here often portrayed as the discoverer and bearer of healing plants to humankind. Who the actual author of this compilation was can no longer be ascertained. In any case, he was not strictly empirical, but appreciated incantations, rites and plant-charms, as the following plates will clearly bear out.

80

Et artemisie leptafyllos suč cum oleo rosario mixtos pungues eos,
desinet dolor 7 tremor 7 omnē uitium tollit.

Nam has tres artemisias. diana dr inuenisse 7 utitutes eap 7 me
dicamina chiro centauro tradidit. Qui pmus deins hebus medicamina
instituit has aut hebtas. ex nole diane h ē artemisie nūcaupauit.

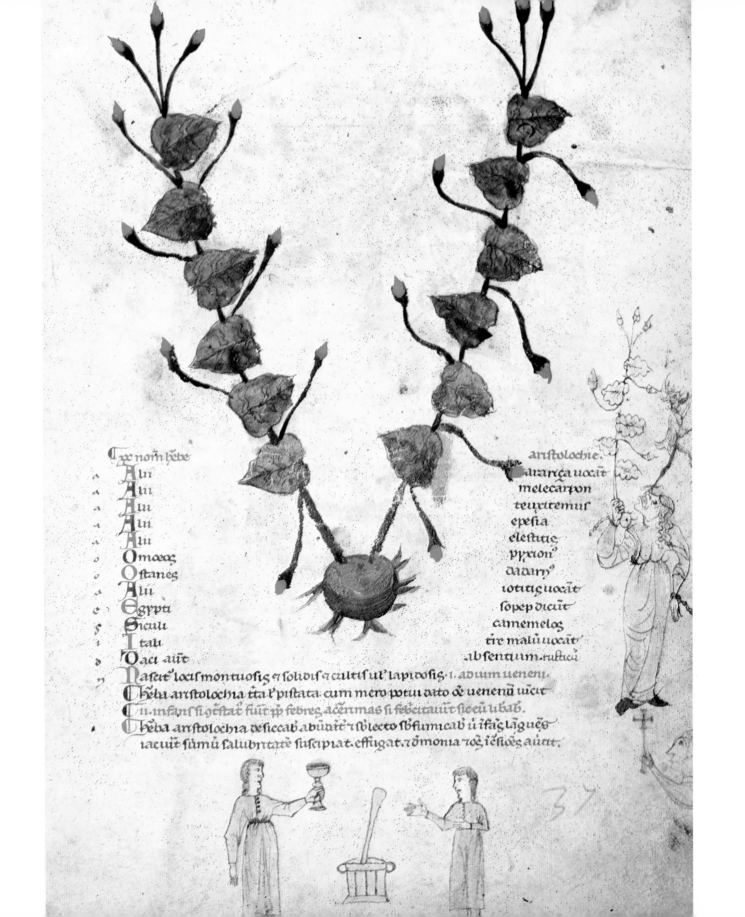

arıſtolochie,

Exc noīñ hĕbe

Alıı
Alıı
Alıı
Alıı
Omœœ
Oſtaneſ
Alıı
Egypti
Sicıli
Itali
Daci aūt

ararça uocāt
melecarpon
teuxitemuſ
epeſia
eleſtttiç
pyxion
dadarıy
iotttiç uocāt
ſopep dicūt
camemeloſ
tır malū uocāt
abſentium ruſtıcı

Naſcit locıſ montuoſıſ ⁊ ſolidıſ ⁊ cultıſ uł lapidoſıſ. i. aduīſ ueneni.
Theba ariſtolochia tta ł piſtata cum mero potui dato de uenenū uīcit
cū ınfanſ ſi gtſtat fuıt ⁊p febreſ acerrimaſ ſi feberitauıt ſıcū libab.
Theba ariſtolochia deſiccab abūıte ⁊ ſubiecto ſubfumicab ū iſtaç lāgueſ
iacuıt ſūmū ſalubrıtate ſuſcipıat. effugat. romonia roõ. ieſtıœ̃ſ auıît.

PLATE 18

Medicina antiqua, fol. 39 recto

This is not the work of a great botanical artist; the picture of the Aristolochia (birth-wort) shown here is quite primitive. The leaves appear to be strung onto the stem. What a masterpiece of late-antique botanical illustration looks like will be shown further on by a plate from the *Wiener Dioskurides* (Plate 26).

The Aristolochia (its German name, Osterluzei [birth-wort] is a folk-etymological conversion of the Greek name "best birth", since this plant played a role in midwifery) does indeed contain valuable substances as the scholar J.R. Möse (Grabner, 1967, pp. 367-8) was able to prove. The infection-inhibiting quality of this plant is based, as careful experiments have shown, on the Aristolochia-acid, which is of late also being given as a medication. In this case a real, empirically proven healing effect is indicated. However, the pen-and-ink drawing on the right-hand margin depicts a woman with chains on her wrist and a grotesquely distorted face holding a birth-wort in her hand; out of her mouth raises a crow-footed devil. The last few lines in the text explain that the birth-wort is effective against demonic attacks. What is pictured in the drawing is the typical form for the portrayal of exorcism in the Middle Ages, the expulsion of the demons from the possessed. The little pointing figure beneath the cured woman indicates the text and is holding a cross to reinforce the Christian character of the scene. The drawing in the margin on the very bottom shows a drug-mortar and the dispension of the medicine.

PLATE 19

Medicina antiqua, fol. 78 verso

The page in the codex prior to the one pictured here shows the plant *Heraclea* and the accompanying text says that wayfarers do not have to fear robbers if they carry this plant with them, since it scares away waylayers. This scene is depicted on this page: on the left a crowded group of eleven men are shown, carrying lances and a *Heraclea* branch. This weapon is evidently effective because in a hilly region in front of the wayfarers, three robbers (latrones) are hiding behind some rocks and give the armed group mean looks. Above the travelers, these words appear: "victor (instead of viator) transit," the wanderer (actually "the victor") passes by. However, these words cannot be seen on this section.

The botanical meaning of "Heraclea" is not quite clear: but to judge by the picture it is not the hogweed *(Heracleum)*. Dr. Grabner, Graz, found in the Tabernaemontanus—the "Sideritis heraclea"—a plant that is pictured in the *Wiener Dioskurides* on fol. 295 verso. There, the name variation "Herklaion" can also be found. But nothing is mentioned about the frightening-off-robbers effect of this plant. It is botanically defined as *Stachys recta, Stachys heraclea* or *Sideritis scordioides* in the text of the *Dioskurides*. It only advises that the leaves heal wounds and inhibit infection.

Below the scene, the plant "strignos" is pictured—*nux vomica, Strychnos nux-vomica* is still used today for medical purposes. The pen-and-ink drawing in the lower margin indicates that the substances of this South-Asian plant were used as a remedy for nose-bleeding.

84

Thebe heraclee grana cū purgat ē in octōs in̄ ū ad caliginē octorum mittis ⁊ statim cum albuginē eam tollis.

Thec. noiē hebe   stringneg ł morella

Cxlviii. nom hebe   imoluz

Clariffima   hecunu eft
homero te   ftante et
uertre el mer   curio adfi
gnate hq. iufu   cuenefiton
demoftrat rou   d̄ radicem
nigramq; ima   zintidine;
cope e .i. cura el ad   dolore matcis

Heba imolu albu grufa epoita dolore matricis pfectiffime aufert.

Comerus auctor   archiategr   mercuri⁹

PLATE 20

Medicina antiqua, fol. 61 verso

The antique-mythological origin of the pharmacopoeia becomes especially clear in this plate which shows the plant "immolum." It is the plant "Moly" which is also pictured in the herbal of Dioskurides. It is known from the Homeric epos, where it says:

> With these words Argeiphontês handed me the charm which he had pulled out of the soil and explained its nature. The root was black, but the flower was milk-white. The gods call it moly: it is hard for mortals to find it, but the gods can do all things.

> (*Odyssey* 10,302-306).

The text to this small plant-picture explains that the plant was used as a remedy for pains in the uterus. Much larger and for the artist apparently more important is the allegorical, mythical scene below it:

Shown on the left is the poet Homer *(Homerus auctor)*. On his knees lies an open book with the inscription "Homerus" on the left side and the Greek "moly" on the right side. The physician (archiater) stands in the middle of the group and turns toward the poet; on the right, Mercurius can be seen, carrying a Moly-plant in each hand. The way his robe is flowing in the wind gave rise to the opinion that the models for the figures thus pictured must have been carriage-driven at full speed. The genitalia were apparently overlooked by the virtuous owner of the book, since here the usual eradication has been omitted. The wings on the ankles and on the top of the head on Hermes have in the medieval transcripts become strange herring-bone shaped out-growths.

The plant that can be identified with Moly in modern botany cannot be clearly determined (Allium Moly?). The more distinctly drawn picture in the herbal of Dioskurides is labeled with "Allium magicum, Allium nigrum" or "Allium Dioscoridis."

PLATE 21

Medicina antiqua, fol. 70 recto

Some of the mythological scenes that demonstrate the special healing quality of a plant seem to have been created by an advertising expert. This picture tells us that *Dictamnus* (dittany) is so powerful that wild animals immediately browse on these plants if they are hit by an arrow—the arrow is then ejected from the wound by its effect and will heal.

This hunting scene with the two horsemen and the dog, who chases a rabbit through the bushes, is stylistically quite appealing. The representation of nature is even more abstract than that of Plate 8 from the *Tacuinum sanitatis* that is included in this book.

The story of the extraordinary healing power of dittany goes back to a type of legend quite familiar to a cultural anthropologist: the wondrous power of the plant was discovered as it was revealed by animals (to mind comes the little plague-bird that pointed out the colt's foot and the burnet saxifrage) or animals were observed regaining their health when instinctively eating a particular plant. For example, dittany is still being used as a folk remedy. The root of this aromatic smelling plant contains Alkaloid Dictamnin: it was believed to be a remedy for stomach-ache and useful as a vermifuge. It was offered by medicine peddlers, along with the root of the peony and sprigs of mistletoe as a remedy for "falling sickness" (epilepsy).

Eiii. qui uenenum sumserit.

H er diptamm sue oitius ectpssus potu ditus efficacissime meder.
tanta aut itus e diptamm uno solum infficiat serpe ec u dubreq;
fuint serpentes psenqa sui eos inffic. Si odore ei adueto fuit ubiq;
fuit serpes moy inffie serpente fere· ⁊ h exeplum. Capria aut ceruus inen
toem si gladio peussi fuit ueniet ad beum diptamnu moy pasett sagitta
exeutiet· ⁊ plaga sanabit eis pascendo diptamnu.

Herbe peonia lunatico iacenti in collo liget statim se eleuat ut sanus.
et si eam secum huit. nunq. ei malu accedit.

Herbe peonie radice pte abligabis de lino eum qui ii. adsciaticos
patitur eu uincies. Hoc e em saluberma. si eu innaue huiis tepestate
opitat si mduig eam utans.

PLATE 22

Medicina antiqua, fol. 72 verso

While some plant-pictures, for example the one of the Aristolchia (Plate 18), are drawn very primitively, some other illustrations in this codex are of great interest from an anthropological point of view. The picture shown here shows the effect of the peony that was mentioned in the previous caption.

The indefinable picture of the plant, which is native to East-Asia, can be found on fol. 71 verso. On fol. 72 recto is a reference saying that according to Homer this plant grows in Crete and Sicily. We, however, are looking at the reproduced page showing a purely magical application of the peony.

The pen-and-ink drawing in the left margin shows a somnambulist (lunaticus) doing a handstand. It is probably supposed to be an epileptic. The picture next to it shows how the "lunatists" were dealt with: a nude patient has his legs locked into a block and his wrists are tied to it. Peony sprigs are wrapped around the patient's neck since, so the text explains, this helps instantly and also has a preventative effect on such ills. In the original codex, the following page shows a ship. If seafarers take along peonies on their journeys they will not be troubled by storms. Aside from this superstitious concept, the poisonous peony in the proper dosage and prescription has no doubt shown real therapeutic results. In folk medicine its root was used for epilepsy, cramps, gout and migrane. The shiny black seeds are hung around the necks of babies to ease their teething (tooth-pearls). In this way the nature of the peony as a charm has been preserved in folk medicine.

PLATE 23

Medicina antiqua, fol. 118 recto

Here again, as before in the *Tacuinum sanitatis* (Plate 5), the "human signature" is the object of this detailed picture. Several stages of the digging process are shown simultaneously. The procedure starts on the right. The root digger walks a dog held by a leash and holds up a treat for him. The reader is already familiar with the method and knows that the root digger is going to tie the leash around the top of the mandrake root. Then he will throw the treat. The dog goes after it and in the process pulls the root out of the ground. On the left bottom, the dog is pictured lying dead, having paid with his life for this magic operation. Next to him is the root, whose scream killed the dog. The scene in the middle shows once more the oversized, human-like root with a headdress made of its leaves. It stands between two root diggers who threaten this anthropomorphous creature of the earth with halberd-like weapons (perhaps digging sticks).

The medical text above the picture names some of the numerous uses for the mandrake. The index-figure points to particularly important paragraphs. The one on top points to a section that is recommending the root for "stigma corporum" (body-rash), since the root is also spotted. The lower figure points out the paragraph that describes the plant as being salutory for pains of the joints *(articulorum dolores)*.

septe dieb; leuit infricitas sn ulceratoe attigit. ad stigmata corporum.
eadem insales candidos reserueta. hanc ipm in medendi inonib; ht.
Radix eius cum aceto ita que inlinita igne sacri curat. Ci. adigne sacrum.
Radix en cum oleo aut cum oleo melle iposita morsu. ad morsu serpentis.
sum serpentis sedat.v. ad chyradas.
Folia eius ita cum aqua z iposita chyradas discutit. vi. ad articulos dolores.
Cum polenta ita z iposita articulos dolore secat. mala a_ psiu pleficiant.
ul edant sopore torpore aut ut uoce auferant faciunt. suc coque ex cortici radici
tte zexpssus inuas fictili ul insole ignito decoquit ita ut absidue agitetur
donec fiat crassitudo mellis. coacte ad medicine usu reponat radice. z sicce re
seruant plurib; usib; pfirtura. Mandragora bnus est masces
et alia e femina. Sinis ut mli bat masen tu et d masen. Sinis puella da ei de
Explicit medicinal librum. femina psate inarui unu.

Therigaticum platonis feliciter.

PLATE 24

Medicina antiqua, fol. 133 recto

While the botanical drawings were not the book illustrator's strong point, other pictures show quite dramatically to this day the vitality and beautiful color of the codex. One of the full-page "pictures of the author" is being presented here since it is an artist's conception of a famous healing expert of antiquity.

Pedanios Dioskurides Anazarbeos is the author of the great pharmacopeia, which, in the form of a picture herbal, is the subject of the following plates. The *Medicina antiqua*, the *Codex 93* of the Austrian National Library, contains an excerpt from the Latin version of the herbal, the tractate "de herbis femineis", which is about female plants. However, the excerpt does not originate from Dioskurides himself but was compiled in the third or fourth century. Part of the text was based on those of Dioskurides, others stem from the Pseudo-Apuleius and other sources. What was meant by a "female plant" is not quite clear—the dioecious concept of modern botany as it appears for example among the Stinging nettle, the hemp, the willow or the poplar, was not known at the time. More likely these are plants that were significant for women for medicinal and cosmetic purposes. The classification of the plants into male and female proved to be very difficult for some conscientious botanist as we shall see (Plate 30).

"Dioscorus" is depicted as a beardless young man in the fashion of the antique pictures of authors. Other such examples are pictures of evangelists which have been preserved from Carolingian times. The subject of this picture is sitting on an upholstered throne in a wall recess with a book on his knees. The inkwell next to him on the right is of shoulder height. The naive love of color in this drawing and the hieratic posture of the ancient physician compensates for some of the lack of skill in the other pictures.

PLATE 25

Wiener Dioskurides, fol. 5 verso

Although one of the "author-pictures" at the front of the large volume, (the fol. 4 verso: Dioskurides and Heuresis, the personification of discovery) is relatively often featured, the small painting reproduced here is much less known. The main reason is the fact that some areas in the center are severely damaged and therefore the picture cannot be easily interpreted.

Pictured on the right is Pedanios Dioskurides with a book in his hand into which he is writing. The codex does not lie on a table but rests on the scholar's right knee. The female in the center is an allegorical figure—Epinoia or Reasoning power. She makes it possible to scientifically utilize the knowledge gained with the help of Heuresis. In her hand she is holding the human-like mandrake-root whose green leaves and red fruit are just barely discernible. On the left we see a young man, dressed in the way of the common people: short tunic, tight pants and dark stockings—the artist of the plant-pictures. He has tacked a sheet of vellum onto the easel and turns around to carefully study the actual model, the mandrake, held by Epinoia.

The beautiful color of the wide border adorned with an acanthus vine and the architectural background reminiscent of theatrical scenery are quite remarkable. Scenery of this kind is also depicted in the mosaics of Ravenna. Historically the originals of these reprints belong to the third or fourth century.

Even in this "ravaged by time" condition one can still imagine the splendor of the codex whose furnishings must have been worthy of a princess. This plate is an excerpt from a picture-page and is reproduced in its original size. However, the following pictures fill the entire height of the 30×37 cm page of the original and had to be reduced in size for reproduction in this volume.

ἀριστολοχίη μακρά

زراوندطويل

amiloti loga
ΑΡΙCΤΟΛΟ   ΧΙ   ΑΜΑ   ΚΡΑ

17ᵛ

PLATE 26

Wiener Dioskurides, fol. 17 verso

Aristolochia makra, aristolochia longo explains the accompanying text. The shape of the plant does not permit the artist to fill out the page; therefore, he places his botanical portrait in the optical center of the page. Besides the "large" *Aristolochia*, the herbal also introduces a smaller *Aristolochia* which is pictured on the next page of the codex. The distinction of both kinds goes back to Crateuas, whereas the actual *Dioskurides* text describes three kinds.

The plant shown here is the birth-wort, with which we became acquainted in an earlier mentioned manuscript. In the lower third of the stem the leaves are drawn toward the front, facing the viewer. Clearly, the space of the picture is perceived illusory; it has depth. The somewhat winding stem is well drawn. Apparently the artist did not have the yellow blossoms in front of him, only the ball-shaped fruits. He did not paint an artist's conception of the *Aristolochia* but a specific live specimen that was already past the blooming stage.

The three kinds of *Aristolochia* of the *Dioskurides* text are to help in a difficult birth, the "boetica" also for asthma and pains in one's side. The plant does indeed contain substances affecting the vascular system, whose composition has become clear to pharmacology only recently. The most important one of those substances is the aristolochia-acid, used against infections and which was mentioned in the discussion of Plate 18 from the artistically less demanding book, *Medicina antiqua*. A comparison of the two plant pictures brings out the great chasm that divides the *Wiener Dioskurides* from the much younger medieval manuscript. Even so, the definitive botanical identification of these detailed pictures is not possible. It is either the *Aristolochia parvifolia* or the *Aristolochia clematitis*.

PLATE 27

Wiener Dioskurides, fol. 20 verso

Artemisia etera polyklonos, Artemisia vulgaris or *arborescens*, sagebrush. This pot-herb, still used to-day, with its small leaves of white, felt-like undersides, is beautifully pictured in the *Dioskurides* codex. Since this is a bushy plant, here again the artist had to pay attention to the depth concept. He solved the problem by shading—the branches facing the viewer are lighter and more delicate.

The codex contains two kinds of *Artemisia,* monoclinous and polyclinous. The specific botanical identification is difficult. The kind shown here is usually identified as *Artemisia aborescens* (mugwort). The text explains that in treatment of females this plant promotes dilation of the vascular ducts, eases menstruation, and has a healing effect on uterine infections and abnormal retention of urine. Even the use of the herb as a poultice on the lower abdomen was recommended. This belief was disputed by the author of the first printed herbal. Also disputed was the notion that a twig tied to one's leg disperses fatigue (therefore the name Biefuss, the German name of mugwort, literally meaning "by the foot"). Brunfels wrote, "Whatever the old heathen conjured up we have imitated just like monkeys, and to this day there is no limit nor end to such and similar superstitions." In the last century, the popular belief still existed that a mugwort with its top pointing down when pinned to the rooftop will guard against lightning and ward off epidemics. The plant was thought to have a "warming and thinning" effect.

100

بنجاسف
أحمر

ἀρτεμησία ετέρα πολύκασον

alia artō.

ΑΡΤΕΜΗCΙΑCΕΤΕΡΑΠΟΛΥΚΛΦΝΟC

† τῶν ἀκανθῶν τῆ καυλοῦ δε
ἐν τ μίκου, δ ἀφνωλθλε ⁚
καὶ φυ γε τ δη λεια δελιασα, κ δε καρον γορυ
ὁ πο μά κη · δ λαφώ δλ. καὶ ὁ ροχὸν ὁ τ ιμετο
τε σ ραδ γε οι ε ρον τα ἀκανθῶ δια φύλλων
ὥ π τῶ δαλλα τ π τον ὁ μβ ρωπ καὶ τῶ δ ρέων
φύλλ ἀ ρ τη τα λα· ὁ τ λ καὶ τὸ ονομα δ
κισθ· ὁ ἀκρ δ ε τοῦ καυλ τ κατ ι και ελεω
ἀ π φύσι· κεφαλη μια εοι κυια ε ηλ
ν το μηκι οδ καμθο δλ· ξηραν ε το δε ⁚
λα κω ι ε γ δε· καὶ οκ λη κι αν η μ τον
την συ τε ει ουλευ. ιι ει ε δε ταυτην ον
οι ρα φε τη εσα καὶ κο πη ισα. κι μ
ρω τη λαβουσα πα ροο γα ον δ λκ
τυ λι ω ρα δα λεω καὶ ου ρι τεω. ει
τι ο ε δ λευ. καὶ ο τι η εδ ρω τη. φ δεν
πλ α πο π τβ ε λ δε ελ ε ε λ ον
λ λ κ πυ ξι δος, το φ με λκ
φα οι δι· μι ρ μι κι ον καὶ δ
κρα χο ρ δ ον αυτο· θ ρμε δ τ
οι ὁ εν τη κεφαλη σκ λη κου
δ ε ο κυ τι ολ θ δ ε ρο μεν· καὶ
π ει α πο τ ο μεν οι δ αι ρι ω με
βε α ι ον ι ι ε ο ρ ω μ τε τ ρ τ αι
δεξ α πλ λ α τ +

PLATE 28

Wiener Dioskurides, fol. 100 recto

Dipsakon, Dipsacus silvestris or *D. fullonum,* weaver-thistle or wild teasel. Pictured here is an example of the second group of plant pictures mentioned in the explanatory text, the less naturalistic ones. However, as we can see by this drawing, the graphic qualities of this group are often quite high even if the purely illustrative aspects suffer. The delineation is powerful and bold, although it does not quite agree with the "physiognomy" of the plant.

While the thistle is known to us for its use to card cloth, the *Dioskurides* text knows of other qualities of this plant; its roots are to be boiled in wine, then mashed and kept in a bronze-container: it heals sores, warts and similar afflictions. But the root in this picture looks quite insignificant and it can be assumed that the artist did not quite know what was of primary importance to a physician. The plant is also called "Krokodilium, Chamäleon, Onokardium, Venus-bad, Venuslippe, and Seseneor by the Egyptians."

PLATE 29

Wiener Dioskurides, fol. 162 verso

Kentaurion to *lepton,* in Latin *Centaurium umbellatum* or *Erythraea centaurium.* During the compilation of the codex according to placement some pages were mixed up and as a result the old text is not next to the picture. A subsequently added text, "Kentaurion to mega," is erroneous as verified by the mirror-image imprint of the real text in the upper margin ("to lepton"). It is the centaury, still appreciated today and used as a drug for stomach ailments.

Here we have a plant still highly praised today, whereas many others from the *Dioskurides* herbal have been forgotten. But in this case the graphic qualities are wanting. However, they are nevertheless sufficient to identify this plant with its almost geometrical branching without difficulty. It seems that the artist did not spend much effort to depict this well-known plant according to its natural model.

In folk medicine the centaury is also used to lower fever (hence the Talin name "Febrifuga"). Moreover, according to Dioskurides, the mashed plant can be used as a healing poultice. The decoction removes "choleric and thick humours." The pressed juice has countless healing qualities. It is recommended to collect the plant in spring by sunrise. We have already come across the mythological derivation of the name "Kentaurion" in the codex (Plate 17) discussed earlier. Compare the picture on page 44!

أنث   لينوزوستين ذكر

اكر زنان خواص كرور زنا
انزابن دواكحروزاكجواميذ
دفق زايس از ماده كحز راغر

OIΛC   ΘΗΛΥΓΟΝΟΝ
OIΛC   ΤΥΡΘΕΣΠΟΝ
OIΛC   ΕΡΜΙΟΥΒΟΤΑΝΗ
OIΛC   ΑΡΓΙΟΝ
OIΛC   ΧΡΥCΙΤΙC
ΛΙΓΥΠΤΙΟΙ   ΑΜΟΦΦ
ΡΩΜΑΙΟΙ   ΕΡΒΑΜΕΡΚΟΥΡΙΑΛΙC
OIΛC   ΜΕΡΚΟΥΡΙΑΛΙCΦΗΜΙΝ
ΛΦΡΟΙ   ΑCΟΥΜΕC

PLATE 30

Wiener Dioskurides, fol. 201 verso

Linozostis theleia, Linozostis arren. Deviating from the usual full page depiction of a single plant, here two plants are drawn next to each other. The botanical interpretation is somewhat problematical. *Linozostis theleia* is mostly identified as either *Mercurialis annua* (the annual mercury) or also as *Mercurialis perennis* (perennial mercury, or in order to distinguish it from the former, also called wood-mercury). *Linozostis arren,* however, especially by the shape of their leaves, resemble more the goose-foot *(Chenopodium).* Apparently it was not quite clear to the illustrator which plant was called for by the text, which seems to have indicated a "male" and a "female" variant of the same species. The artist was probably forced to find a similar plant and accomodated himself by selecting one that he found to be most likely related. Also the Synonyma of the plant names shows that the differentiation was difficult even in antiquity. "Chrysitis" and "Parthenion" appear in both lists. However, the difference was clear to the Egyptians. They know "Allopho" and "Aphlopho."

The mercury plant is a euphorbiacee without the milky juice, which was highly regarded in antiquity. Both "male" and "female" plants are supposedly suitable for a decoction, which is effective for cleaning the body of bile and watery matter. But more importantly, it enabled one to pre-determine the sex of unborn children. If the leaves of the "male" plants are finely crushed and then drunk or after menstruation applied as suppositories, a male child will be conceived, whereas the "female" plant favors a female child. This belief was often taken quite seriously in antiquity. Its discovery was ascribed to Mercury. However, as we have shown above, the botanical identification being difficult, the verification of this tradition would not seem very easy . . .

In the *Universal-Lexicon* (Vol. 3, 1733) by Zedler, the differentiation between the male and the female mercury (*Mercurialis mas* and *Mercurialis femina*) is carefully executed, but the sex-determining power is no longer mentioned. The plants "containing much oil, phlegm and essential salt", "are primarily used for enemas" but also generally "for sterility." The original designation probably served to differentiate between the meadow-mercury, blooming from June to October and the wood-mercury, blooming from April to May. Both kinds are poisonous, but are not used any more for medicinal purposes.